Workforce Mathematics 1

Student Text

Vocational occupations icon design courtesy of the Vocational Education Services Project directed by Dale Law and John Smith of the University of Illinois.

Published and Distributed by:
   CORD Communications, Inc.
   P.O. Box 21206, Waco, Texas 76702-1206
   324 Kelly Drive, Waco, Texas 76710
   (817) 776-1822 Fax (817) 776-3906

Printed in USA

ISBN 1-55502-847-0
CORD Workforce Mathematics 1

Preface

The demand for continuing education has never been greater. The catalyst for this demand is the prolific expansion of technology in the workplace. To benefit from this expansion, you must have a strong working knowledge of mathematics. We have designed the **CORD Workforce Mathematics** series to meet your needs as an adult learner. Specifically, this series will provide you an effective and time-sensitive means for learning the basic mathematics skills required in today's high-performance workplaces.

The **CORD Workforce Mathematics** series covers a broad range of mathematical topics and consists of five books.

Book 1: CORD Workforce Mathematics 1

Book 2: CORD Workforce Mathematics 2

Book 3: CORD Workforce Mathematics—Algebra

Book 4: CORD Workforce Mathematics—Geometry

Book 5: CORD Workforce Mathematics—Enrichment

These books contain mathematical concepts that are used in the workplace. By mastering these concepts, you will develop a better understanding of your current job and the confidence to pursue jobs that demand higher skills.

We have designed the **CORD Workforce Mathematics** series to make mathematics more useful and meaningful for you—and reduce some of the "math anxiety" we all feel at one time or another. Each book in the series contains numerous workplace examples that span a full range of occupation—plumbing, business, carpentry, landscaping, and so on. From these examples, you will learn mathematical skills while simultaneously practicing problem solving in real-world scenarios.

Next, you'll have a chance to practice what you've learned. You'll do this in a laboratory activity that involves measurement and problem solving. You'll apply the mathematics skills to practical problems. These problems are the kind people have to solve every day—in stores, factories, repair centers, hospitals, laboratories, or at home.

You'll learn to use mathematics, little by little, problem by problem. And in the process, you will build confidence in yourself and open the door to future job success.

The CORD Project Staff

Learning Path

1. Read the "Introduction" section of each chapter.

2. Take part in the class discussions.

3. Read the explanations and examples in the text and follow the directions to write answers to the questions.

4. Do the assigned laboratory activity.

5. Complete the assigned exercises.

6. Measure your progress by taking the chapter test.

Some Signals to Help You Learn

The following signals help you know what to do as you read the text:

 Think this through. Spend a little extra time on this idea.

 Write your answer on your paper.

 Carry out the calculations.

 Learn this key rule or definition.

 Estimate and ask yourself if this answer makes sense.

 Compare your answer to the given one and make any needed changes.

Table of Contents

Chapter 4: Learning Problem-Solving Techniques   105

Chapter 5: Estimating Answers   133

Chapter 6: Measuring in English and Metric Units   161

Learning the Skills

Practicing the Skills

Chapter 7: Using Graphs, Charts, and Tables   199

Learning the Skills

Practicing the Skills

Chapter 8: Dealing with Data   247

Learning the Skills

Practicing the Skills

Glossary   289

Appendices   301

Chapter 1

Getting to Know Your Calculator

How to use your calculator to add, subtract, multiply, and divide fractions, decimals, and mixed numbers

Prerequisites

This is the first of three preparatory chapters for the **CORD Workforce Mathematics** series. This chapter provides a basic review of arithmetic operations and the use of a calculator. To complete this chapter, you should:

- be familiar with fractions, mixed numbers, and decimals

- know how to operate a calculator

- have a scientific calculator with parenthesis keys

To Master This Chapter

Read the text and answer all questions. Complete the assigned activity and exercises. Work the problems on the end-of-chapter test at a satisfactory level.

Chapter Objectives

Working through this chapter will help you to learn to:

1. Enter numbers, fractions, and decimals into a calculator and read the output displayed by a calculator.

2. Use the parenthesis keys on a calculator.

3. Add, subtract, multiply, and divide fractions with a calculator.

4. Add, subtract, multiply, and divide mixed numbers with a calculator.

5. Add, subtract, multiply, and divide decimals with a calculator.

LEARNING THE SKILLS

INTRODUCTION

How many ways can you get across the idea of "five"?

Figure 1
Ways to say five

 Make a list on your own paper of ways to write "five." Which of the ways on this list could you use with your calculator? Draw circles around those that you could "key" into your calculator.

Look at the display window of the calculator. That's where the calculator "writes" or displays numbers. How does the calculator write "five"? Does it display it as a word? As a number? As a fraction?

You already know that you can't type the word "five" into the calculator. (It's not like a typewriter.) But as Figure 1 shows, there may be several ways to "key in" numbers that end up as "5" in the display window.

Numbers you'll work with on the calculator

You will use several different types of numbers with your calculator. They are:

- whole numbers
- fractions
- mixed numbers
- decimals

You probably know what these numbers are, but let's review them just to make sure.

Whole numbers are made up of the set of counting numbers and zero (0, 1, 2, 3, 4, 5, ...). Examples of whole numbers are 7, 16, 143, 1792, and so on.

Fractions are numbers such as $\frac{1}{3}$, $\frac{3}{4}$, and $\frac{20}{5}$. They are written with one whole number over (or divided by) another whole number. The number on the top is called the numerator. The one on the bottom is called the denominator.

- Fractions are described as either proper fractions or improper fractions. A **proper fraction** is one like $\frac{3}{8}$, $\frac{1}{5}$, or $\frac{8}{9}$. For a proper fraction, the numerator is always **less** in value than the denominator.

- An **improper fraction** is one like $\frac{8}{3}$, $\frac{9}{8}$, or $\frac{10}{10}$. For an improper fraction, the numerator is always **equal to or greater** in value than the denominator.

Mixed numbers are combinations of whole numbers and fractions—such as $9\frac{7}{8}$ and $2\frac{3}{4}$. When you read a mixed number you say "nine and seven-eighths" or "two and three fourths." You identify both the whole number and the fraction.

Decimals are numbers such as 1.5, 0.25, 273.4, and so on. You can recognize decimals because they always involve the decimal point (period) somewhere in the number.

In your job, you may often need to use whole numbers, fractions, mixed numbers, and decimals to solve problems with your calculator. In this chapter you'll explore ways to key whole numbers, fractions, mixed numbers, and decimals into the calculator. You'll also learn how to "tell" the calculator what to do—and how to interpret the answers it gives back to you.

GETTING STARTED WITH A CALCULATOR

Look closely at the keyboard of your calculator. The face of a typical scientific calculator is shown in Figure 2. Generally, scientific calculators are characterized by having trigonometric functions (sin, cos, tan), power functions (y^x, $\sqrt[x]{y}$), and scientific notation (EE). Some may also be programmable and support statistical and business computations.

Usually you key in (input) numbers when you begin to use the calculator. Will it accept all the kinds of numbers you can write?

Let's do some experimenting to find out.

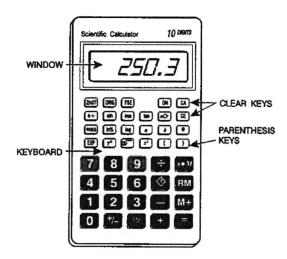

Figure 2
A scientific calculator

First, how do you turn your calculator **ON**? Find the key that does this.

When the calculator is ON and ready to use, you will see a "0." or simply a "0" in the window. You may see also the small letters DEG to the left. You can ignore the DEG for now.

If the window does not show "0," you must clear the window. Most calculators have more than one key to clear the window. A common one is labeled as CA (Clear All) or AC (All Clear). Others are labeled as C, AC/ON, ON/C and CE/C. Locate the one that clears the window for your calculator.

To clear the window, press the key you've located. This gets rid of all old work and clears the calculator so it is ready to begin a new problem. Sometimes you may need to press the "clear window" key several times before you see a "0" in the window.

What is the difference between keys labeled as CA, C, and CE? Think of it this way:

- The CA (or AC) key clears everything; it's just like erasing the entire chalkboard.

- The "C" key clears everything except what you may have stored in memory; it is like erasing the whole chalkboard except the notice in the corner that is labeled "Do Not Erase."

- The CE key clears only the last entry that you made— the last number key you pushed; that's like erasing only the last number you wrote on the chalkboard.

Saying it another way:
      CA clears everything.
      C clears everything except memory.
      CE clears only the last entry.

How do you enter numbers INTO a calculator?

Experiment with your calculator if you want to. You can't hurt it by pressing the keys, but it will break if you drop it or strike it! After you finish experimenting, press the CA (clear everything) key to clear out all the work you did.

                                       CORD Workforce Mathematics 1

See how many ways you can enter five into the calculator. Press the Clear key between each one. When you have finished this experiment, try these:

> Press the 5 key. What do you see in the window?
> Press the Clear key.
> Press the 5 key and then the decimal key. (The decimal key is the one with the tiny dot.) What do you see?

Press Clear again. Then press 5, the decimal key, and zero. You can add as many zeros as you like after the decimal.

All of these are ways the calculator can say five:

> 5.
> 5.0
> 5.00000

Press Clear and then enter 05 with no decimal. What does the window say? Does it make any difference how many zeros you enter before (to the left of) a number?

Press Clear. Then press the 2 key, the plus (+) key, the 3 key, and finally, the equal (=) key. Another way to say five!

Press Clear. Now try entering 35 and then pressing the divide (÷) key, then 7, and finally the = key. Written out that looks like 35 ÷ 7 = . Still another way to say "five."

How many ways do you think you can put "five" **into** the calculator? (How many different ways can you press keys so 5 appears in the window?)

How does a calculator display numbers?

How many ways do you think you can read "five" out of the calculator? (How many different window displays will you read as 5?)

You saw 5.0 (or 5. followed by several zeros) in the window as you tried the previous entries. Can you make 5 appear in the window in some other way? Is there any way to show five in the window other than 5., or 5. followed by one or more zeros?

No matter whether you enter fractions, whole numbers, or decimals into a calculator, the answer always is displayed as a decimal. If you enter 15 ÷ 3, the answer is 5. If you enter 27 ÷ 4, the answer is 6.75. If you enter 17 ÷ 7, the answer is 2.42857143—or 2.428571429, depending on whether your calculator displays answers with nine or ten digits. In each case the answer in the window appears as a decimal.

What do you do with an answer like 2.428571429? You know that in most cases you won't need that many digits in the answer. So, when you divide 17 by 7, for example, you will have to decide how much of the calculator answer to use. The calculator won't do that for you.

Let's decide on a reasonable rule for handling long calculator answers. Unless the problem you're working on requires answers to many places, **round** an answer like 2.428571249 to **two places to the right** of the decimal point. Do this as follows:

- If the third number to the right of the decimal point is 5 or greater, simply **add one to** the second number beyond the decimal point and drop all numbers to the right of it.

- If the third number to the right of the decimal point is less than 5, **leave the second number as it is** and drop all numbers to the right of it.

If you follow these rules, the number 2.428571249 becomes 2.43. What number do you get when you round the 10-place number 2.413487002 to two places to the right of the decimal point?

Does the order of entering numbers into a calculator matter?

Suppose you are asked to carry out the operation 3 + 5 = on the calculator. You know that 3 + 5 = means you are to add 3 and 5. So you do the following:

Turn the calculator ON
Press the 3 key
Press the + key
Press the 5 key
Press the = key
Read the answer 8. in the window.

What **order** did you follow as you carried out this operation? First you entered the 3, then the 5. What would happen if you changed the order? That is, what answer would you get if you pressed the 5 key, then the + key, and then the 3 key? The answer would be the SAME. That's because 3 + 5 is the same as 5 + 3. Both give 8 for the answer.

You can say, then, that **when numbers are to be added,** the **order** in which you enter the numbers into the calculator **doesn't matter**.

Now what about **subtraction**? If you want to carry out the operation 10 − 5, do you have to put the 10 in before the 5? Or can you put the 5 in before the 10? Try it and see. First solve 10 − 5 =. Then do 5 − 10 =. Are the answers different? They **are** different because 10 − 5 = 5 and 5 − 10 = −5. The numbers 5 and −5 are NOT the same. One is a positive number; the other is a negative number.

So, now you can say also that when two numbers are to be **subtracted,** the **order does matter.** The operation must be carried out in the same order as is stated in the problem.

How about **multiplication**? Or **division**? Try to figure out what the rules are for order in multiplying and dividing. Pick a simple multiplication problem that involves two whole numbers. Multiply them out, first one way, then the other. Does the order matter? Then try a simple division problem. Does the order matter? After you've finished your experiment, copy and complete the following statements. Write the correct word (does or doesn't) in the blank space.

- When I multiply numbers, the order in which I choose to enter the numbers into my calculator _____ matter.

- When I divide numbers, the order in which I choose to enter the numbers into my calculator _____ matter.

WORKING WITH FRACTIONS

Now that you've learned how to enter numbers into a calculator and read the answers given by the calculator, let's begin carrying out operations with fractions. As you recall, fractions are numbers like ⅓, ⅜, and ¹⁷⁄₉—written with a numerator (top number) divided by a denominator (bottom number).

Entering fractions

Earlier you entered the problem 35 ÷ 7 = to get 5. You can write this same problem in a different way. The expression 35 ÷ 7 (35 divided by 7) also can be written as the fraction ³⁵⁄₇.

 How would you enter the fraction ¼ (one-fourth) into your calculator?

Now enter the fraction ⅓ (one-third).

To find the value of a fraction with your calculator, press the keys for the top number, then the ÷ key, then the keys for the bottom number, and then the = key.

Enter these fractions (remember to Clear between fractions!):

> three-fourths
> ⁶⁄₈
> ³⁶⁄₄₈

Did you get the same number in the window for all three of these problems?

Watch the decimal point!

What number do you get when you enter ³⁵⁄₇ or 35 ÷ 7?

What number do you get when you enter ½ or 1 ÷ 2?

The position of the decimal point makes a lot of difference. Would you rather be paid ³⁵⁄₇ dollars an hour or ½ dollar an hour?

The only difference between $^{35}\!/_7$ and $^1\!/_2$ in the calculator window is the placement of the decimal point. That tiny dot means the difference, in this case, between fifty cents an hour and five dollars an hour. So it's a good idea to pay attention to that decimal point!

When you enter a fraction in the calculator, the display window does not show a fraction. It shows a decimal! Now let's look at fractions written the way the calculator can write them.

Fractions equal to one

After you Clear, find the value of $^{12}\!/_{12}$ with your calculator. What answer do you get? Enter $^5\!/_5$ and then $^7\!/_7$ and then these:

$$^9\!/_9 \, , \, ^3\!/_3 \, , \, ^2\!/_2$$

The fraction $^{12}\!/_{12}$ (or twelve-twelfths) is another way to say one. So is five-fifths, seven-sevenths, three-thirds, or two-halves.

TWELVE–TWELFTHS ($^{12}\!/_{12}$)

FOUR–FOURTHS ($^4\!/_4$)

FIVE–FIFTHS ($^5\!/_5$)

TWO–HALVES ($^2\!/_2$)

Figure 3
Ways to say one

Fractions less than one

Fractions less than one (for instance, $^{11}/_{12}$, $^3/_5$, $^4/_7$, $^2/_9$, $^1/_2$) all have numbers on the top that are smaller in value than the numbers on the bottom. As you recall, such fractions are called **proper** fractions.

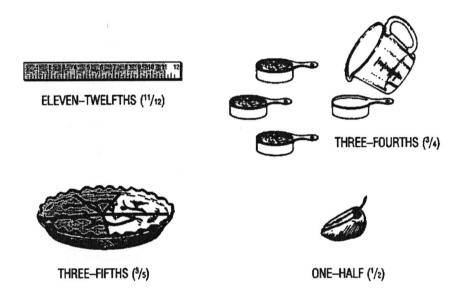

ELEVEN–TWELFTHS ($^{11}/_{12}$)

THREE–FOURTHS ($^3/_4$)

THREE–FIFTHS ($^3/_5$)

ONE–HALF ($^1/_2$)

Figure 4
Fractions less than one

 Enter some of the proper fractions shown in Figure 4 into your calculator.

A proper fraction names a number **less than one**. For instance, a proper fraction could have less than twelve-twelfths (for example, $^{11}/_{12}$ or $^7/_{12}$). A proper fraction also could have less than nine-ninths— for instance, $^8/_9$ or $^2/_9$.

When you enter a proper fraction into the calculator, what kind of number do you get in the window? *Where* is the decimal point for any number you get by entering a proper fraction?

On your own paper, complete this sentence:

When I enter a proper fraction into the calculator, I get a number in the window that always has a decimal point located _____.

Fractions greater than one

What about fractions that are *not* proper? As you've learned, they are called improper fractions. An improper fraction has a numerator that is equal to or greater in value than the denominator. The value of an improper fraction is always *equal to or more* than one. For instance, $^{13}/_{12}$ is an improper fraction. Notice that the top number (13) is larger in value than the bottom number (12).

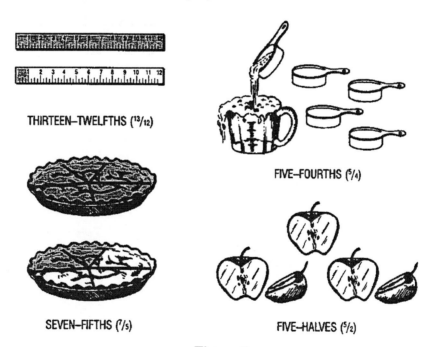

THIRTEEN–TWELFTHS ($^{13}/_{12}$)

FIVE–FOURTHS ($^5/_4$)

SEVEN–FIFTHS ($^7/_5$)

FIVE–HALVES ($^5/_2$)

Figure 5
Fractions more than one

Calculating with fractions

The calculator handles fractions as easily as it handles whole numbers. If you know how to enter fractions into the calculator, you can add, subtract, multiply, and divide fractions rather quickly. Let's try some examples.

Example 1:
Adding fractions

Add the fractions $\frac{7}{8}$ and $\frac{20}{32}$ [$\frac{7}{8} + \frac{20}{32} =$].

Follow the steps outlined below:

Turn the calculator ON; Clear the display.
Press the 7 key
Press the ÷ key
Press the 8 key
Press the + key
Press the 2 key and the 0 key to enter the number 20
Press the ÷ key
Press the 3 key and the 2 key to enter the number 32
Press the = key

Did you get 1.5 for an answer? If not, try again. Would you have gotten the same answer if you had changed the order and added $\frac{20}{32} + \frac{7}{8}$?

Example 2:
Subtracting fractions

Subtract $\frac{3}{16}$ from $\frac{8}{32}$ [$\frac{8}{32} - \frac{3}{16} =$].

Follow the steps outlined below:

Turn the calculator ON; Clear the display.
Press the 8 key
Press the ÷ key
Press the 3 key and the 2 key for the number 32
Press the − key
Press the 3 key
Press the ÷ key
Press the 1 key and the 6 key for the number 16
Press the = key

Did you get 0.0625? If not, try again. Would you have gotten the same answer if you had changed the order and carried out the operation [$\frac{3}{16} - \frac{8}{32} =$] ?

Example 3:
Multiplying fractions

Multiply $\frac{3}{8} \times \frac{4}{3}$. (Does the order matter?)

Follow the steps outlined below:

Turn the calculator ON; Clear the display.
Press the 3 key
Press the ÷ key
Press the 8 key
Press the × key
Press the 4 key
Press the ÷ key
Press the 3 key
Press the = key

Did you get 0.5? Now try multiplying $\frac{4}{3} \times \frac{3}{8}$. Did you get the same answer?

Example 4:
Dividing fractions

Divide $\frac{2}{5}$ by $\frac{1}{2}$ [$\frac{2}{5} \div \frac{1}{2}$ =].

This calculation has a "trap" built in. If you follow the same set of steps you did in the previous examples, you will get the **wrong** answer. That's because you would key in the numbers and operations as follows:

$$2 \div 5 \div 1 \div 2.$$

The calculator interprets that chain of operations as $\frac{2}{5}$ divided by 1 (answer is $\frac{2}{5}$) and then that answer ($\frac{2}{5}$) divided by 2 (answer is $\frac{1}{5}$). But in fact you want $\frac{2}{5}$ divided by $\frac{1}{2}$—for which the correct answer is $\frac{4}{5}$ or 0.8. How do you "tell" the calculator that you want to divide by the fraction $\frac{1}{2}$? You do it by using the parentheses on the calculator. That is, you need to "tell" the calculator that you want to solve the problem [$\frac{2}{5} \div (\frac{1}{2})$ =].

Do this as follows:
Turn the calculator ON; Clear the display.
Press the 2 key
Press the ÷ key
Press the 5 key
Press the ÷ key
Press the left parenthesis "(" key
Press the 1 key
Press the ÷ key
Press the 2 key
Press the right parenthesis ")" key
Press the = key

Did you get 0.8?

If you try the same steps but leave out the two steps that involve the parenthesis keys, you'll get 0.2, the **wrong** answer.

When dividing a fraction by a fraction, always enclose the second fraction by left and right parentheses.

WORKING WITH MIXED NUMBERS

What is a mixed number? A **mixed number** is partly a fraction and partly a whole number. For example, 5¾ (five and three-fourths) is a mixed number. The first part, 5, is a whole number and the last part, ¾, is a proper fraction.

You can think of the proper fraction ¾ as a division problem. You already know this because you enter ¾ into the calculator with the key that means "divided by." That is, ¾ is entered as 3 ÷ 4.

The mixed number 5¾ means "the whole number 5 added to the fraction ¾" and the fraction ¾ means "3 divided by 4." Putting this all together:

5¾ means 5 plus ¾

or   5¾ means 5 + (3 ÷ 4).

The parentheses around "3 ÷ 4" make it clear that 3 is to be divided by 4, and that the result is to be added to 5.

Using parentheses with mixed numbers

You've already learned that when a **fraction** is to be **divided** by a **fraction**, like ⅖ ÷ ½, you need **parentheses** around the second fraction to get the correct answer.

Do we need parentheses when we combine a fraction and a whole number? Let's see what difference parentheses make in this case.

Try the three following problems with **your** calculator:

    a. 5 + 3 ÷ 4 = ?   (no parentheses)

    b. 5 + (3 ÷ 4) = ?   (parentheses around 3 ÷ 4)

    c. (5 + 3 ÷ 4) = ?   (parentheses around everything)

If your calculator gave you the same answer (5.75) for each of the three problems, you are using a **scientific** calculator. It has been programmed to divide before adding. Therefore, it automatically divided 3 by 4 first, and then added that answer to 5 to get 5.75.

If your calculator gave you an answer of 2 for problem A, you do not have a scientific calculator. With such a calculator, to get the correct answer of 5.75, you must divide 3 by 4 first (to get 0.75) and then add that result to 5. (You are strongly encouraged to use a scientific calculator—with parenthesis keys on the keyboard—for the course in **CORD Workforce Mathematics 1.**)

What have you learned by working the three problems above? You've learned that with a scientific calculator you don't need parentheses to get the correct answer when you enter a mixed number. You also don't need parentheses when you **add** mixed numbers together. But **you do need the parentheses** around mixed numbers—as in Problem C—when you **subtract, multiply,** and **divide** them. If you don't use the parentheses, you'll get the wrong answer. For a scientific calculator with parentheses, remember these rules:

- You **do not need** to enter mixed numbers **with parentheses** when you **add** them.

- You **do need** to enter mixed numbers **with parentheses** when you **subtract, multiply,** and **divide** them.

Adding mixed numbers

Let's practice using the calculator to operate on mixed numbers. Work through the following examples.

Example 5:
Measuring floor molding

Marie has torn up the carpet in a room. She now needs to put quarter-round molding over the gap where the floor meets the wall. She measures, leaving out the doors and other places where there will be no molding. She finds that she needs pieces of molding of these lengths:

$8\frac{3}{4}$ ft
$6\frac{1}{2}$ ft
$2\frac{1}{4}$ ft
$2\frac{5}{8}$ ft
$1\frac{3}{4}$ ft
$5\frac{3}{8}$ ft

Marie wants to use her calculator to add these lengths and find the total. She can do this in more than one way. The next section shows you four different ways to do a problem that adds mixed numbers. Try each one, and then decide which method you like the best.

Method One: Marie begins by adding all the whole numbers. Marie clears her calculator and presses the 8 key and then the + key and then the 6 key, + key, 2 key, + key, 2 key, + key, 1 key, + key, 5 key, and, finally, the = key.

Try this on your calculator and see what you get:

$$8 + 6 + 2 + 2 + 1 + 5 \ =$$

Marie next adds the fractions by making a rough estimate. She notices that ⅝ + ⅜ is ⁸⁄₈ or 1.

She sees that ¾ + ¼ is ⁴⁄₄ or 1.

That leaves ¾ + ½ which she estimates roughly as 1. That gives her an estimated total of 24 + 1 + 1 + 1 feet, or 27 feet.

Method Two: Marie can add the fractions *exactly* with a little thought. Again she adds ⅝ + ⅜ to get ⁸⁄₈ or 1, and ¾ + ¼ is ⁴⁄₄ or 1. To add ¾ + ½ she thinks "½ is the same as ²⁄₄," so she adds ¾ + ²⁄₄ to get ⁵⁄₄ or 1¼.

The fractions add to 1 + 1 + 1¼, or 3¼ feet. The whole numbers add to 24 feet, so the total length is *exactly* 27¼ feet.

Marie likes to use her calculator for this addition, especially for a long list.

She decides to add the lengths again with her calculator to check her mental arithmetic.

Method Three: She adds ¾ + ½ by entering the following chain:

$$3 \div 4 + 1 \div 2 \ =$$

Do this with your calculator and see what you get.

When Marie did this in her head she got $1\frac{1}{4}$. On the calculator she gets 1.25. Remember that the calculator can "read" fractions but it can give answers only in decimals. Is $1\frac{1}{4}$ the same number as 1.25? How can you be sure?

To add all the fractions at once, enter these keys into your calculator:

$$3 \div 4 + 1 \div 2 + 1 \div 4 + 5 \div 8 + 3 \div 4 + 3 \div 8 =$$

and then add all the whole numbers to get the total.

Compare your answer with the one Marie got in Method Two. If you didn't get 27.25 feet, clear your calculator and try again. Take it a little slower this time!

Method Four: Marie could have done all the adding at one time by entering each number, whole number plus the fraction, in the calculator. To do this, enter the whole number part plus the fraction (numerator ÷ denominator), plus the next whole number, and so forth.

Try it now:

$$8\frac{3}{4} + 6\frac{1}{2} + 2\frac{1}{4} + 2\frac{5}{8} + 1\frac{3}{4} + 5\frac{3}{8} =$$

Did you get the same answer as before? If not, try again, slowly and carefully. **Remember, you don't have to include parentheses around mixed numbers when you add them.**

Now that you know several ways to add a list of fractions, try this next problem. Use the way you like best.

Study Activity: JoAnn plans to build some shelves for a stereo component cabinet. She already has the frame. She knows that she needs six pieces of shelving. What is the total length JoAnn needs?

30½ inches
23¼ inches
28¼ inches
7½ inches
28¼ inches
14¾ inches

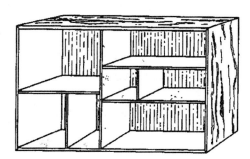

You may get a decimal answer, or a mixed-number answer, depending on the way you choose to work the problem. If you get a mixed-number answer, use your calculator to change it to a decimal answer.

If the lumberyard sells the shelving only in 8-foot lengths, how many boards will JoAnn have to buy?

Subtracting mixed numbers

As long as you enter mixed numbers in the correct order—**and surround each one with parentheses**—you can subtract mixed numbers easily with your calculator.

Try subtracting these mixed numbers:

$$3\tfrac{1}{3} - 2\tfrac{1}{4}$$

Example 6:
Subtracting mixed numbers

To do this (with your scientific calculator), follow these steps:

Turn the calculator ON; Clear the display
Press the left parenthesis key
Press the 3 key
Press the + key
Press the 1 key
Press the ÷ key
Press the 3 key
Press the right parenthesis key
Press the – key
Press the left parenthesis key
Press the 2 key
Press the + key
Press the 1 key
Press the ÷ key
Press the 4 key
Press the right parenthesis key
Press the = key

Did you get 1.083333 ....? If you round this answer to two places to the right of the decimal point, what should it be?

Try this one on your own. Be sure to use the parentheses.

$$7\tfrac{3}{4} - 4\tfrac{5}{8} =$$

Since 7 − 4 is 3, you knew before you started that the answer would be about 3. Did your answer with the calculator come out close to 3? What is your answer rounded to two decimal places to the right of the decimal point?

Multiplying and dividing mixed numbers

If you've learned how to use the parentheses on your calculator, you can multiply and divide mixed numbers just as easily as you can subtract them. Let's look at $12\frac{3}{4}$ times $1\frac{2}{3}$ or $12\frac{3}{4} \times 1\frac{2}{3} =$.

What you want to do is the following:

$$(12 + 3 \text{ divided by } 4) \times (1 + 2 \text{ divided by } 3)$$

Write out a step-by-step program, like the one shown above for subtraction. Then carry out the steps on your calculator.

The correct answer is 21.25. Is that what you got?

Now, just for fun, enter the same problem with no parentheses, like this:

$$12 + 3 \text{ divided by } 4 \times 1 + 2 \text{ divided by } 3 \text{ equals } \underline{\ \ ?\ \ }.$$

What did you get for an answer? Is it the same as before? The parentheses do make a difference!

Now let's try dividing mixed numbers. Do the following problems. Don't forget the parentheses!

$$6\frac{2}{3} \div 3\frac{1}{3} =$$

$$12\frac{3}{4} \div 1\frac{2}{3} =$$

WORKING WITH DECIMALS

You have used your calculator to add, subtract, multiply, and divide fractions and mixed numbers. Working with decimals on the calculator is even easier. That's because you can enter decimals into the calculator easily—and read the calculator answer directly as a decimal.

Adding decimals

Work through this problem.

Example 7:
Calculating mileage

A delivery person made six trips in the company car this week. What is the total mileage if the log book shows the mileages listed in Figure 6?

First, estimate the answer. You could do this by adding the whole numbers (before the decimal) either in your head or on your calculator. What do you get? Based on this estimate, do you think an exact answer near 55 is reasonable?

For an exact answer, add the decimal numbers in Figure 6 on your calculator. To do this press the keys, including the decimal point key, exactly as the numbers and the decimal points appear in the problem.

MILEAGE LOG

MONTH 6 DAY 22 YEAR 95	BUSINESS MILES TRAVELED
ODOMETER READING	
END OF TRIP 26545.4	
LESS BEGINNING OF TRIP 26539.7	
TOTAL BUSINESS MILES	5.7
MONTH 6 DAY 22 YEAR 95	
ODOMETER READING	
END OF TRIP 26775.1	
LESS BEGINNING OF TRIP 26760.8	
TOTAL BUSINESS MILES	12.3
MONTH 6 DAY 24 YEAR 95	
ODOMETER READING	
END OF TRIP 26923.1	
LESS BEGINNING OF TRIP 26918.3	
TOTAL BUSINESS MILES	4.8
MONTH 6 DAY 27 YEAR 95	
ODOMETER READING	
END OF TRIP 27187.5	
LESS BEGINNING OF TRIP 27177.4	
TOTAL BUSINESS MILES	10.1
MONTH 6 DAY 27 YEAR 95	
ODOMETER READING	
END OF TRIP 27209.8	
LESS BEGINNING OF TRIP 27194.4	
TOTAL BUSINESS MILES	15.4
MONTH 6 DAY 28 YEAR 95	
ODOMETER READING	
END OF TRIP 27262.5	
LESS BEGINNING OF TRIP 27255.0	
TOTAL BUSINESS MILES	7.5
MONTH DAY YEAR	
ODOMETER READING	
END OF TRIP	
LESS BEGINNING OF TRIP	
TOTAL BUSINESS MILES	
TOTAL FOR WEEK	

Figure 6
Adding miles

Remember to clear before you start, and to press the + key between each number.

Compare the calculator answer to your estimate. If they are not about the same value (within 2 or 3 miles of each other), do the problem again.

Subtracting decimals

Subtracting decimals is just as easy as adding decimals. For example, suppose you buy two items at the grocery store for $2.73 and $5.87. You want to hand the cashier enough money and you also want to be sure you receive the correct change.

First, estimate how much you've spent. To be on the safe side, round $2.73 up to $3.00 and $5.87 up to $6.00. Based on your estimate, will a ten-dollar bill cover your purchases?

You give the cashier a ten-dollar bill. How much change should you get back? (Assume that tax is 56 cents.)

You can get the answer by two different calculations. Which of the two ways shown below did you use?

$$\$10.00 - \$2.73 - \$5.87 - \$0.56 \ =$$

or $$\$10.00 - (\$2.73 + \$5.87 + \$0.56) \ =$$

Do they both give the same answer? What happens if you forget the **parentheses** in the second method?

Multiplying and dividing decimals

Now try multiplying and dividing decimals. Copy each of the following problems on a separate sheet of paper. Round your answers to 2 decimal places to the right of the decimal point.

$$20.5 \times 3.1416 \ =$$

$$0.002 \times 178.3 \ =$$

$$39.2 \div 57.6 \ =$$

$$7.8 \div 0.012 \ =$$

PRACTICING WITH YOUR CALCULATOR

In this chapter, you've used your calculator to add, subtract, multiply, and divide these kinds of numbers:

- whole numbers
- fractions
- mixed numbers
- decimals

You've also learned how to use parentheses and how to round long decimal numbers you sometimes get from the calculator. Let's practice one more time.

Copy and solve the following problems with the help of your calculator. Answer the questions that are next to the problems.

1. Adding

   a. $\frac{3}{8} + \frac{15}{20} = ?$ Are parentheses needed?

   b. $3\frac{2}{5} + 50\frac{3}{8} = ?$ Are parentheses needed?

   c. $5.7 + 108.23 = ?$ Does the order of keying in the numbers matter?

2. Subtracting

   a. $\frac{15}{20} - \frac{5}{8} = ?$ Does the order of keying in the fractions matter?

   b. $50\frac{3}{8} - 3\frac{1}{4} = ?$ Are parentheses needed?

   c. $108.23 - 5.10 = ?$ Does the order matter?

3. Multiplying

   a. $\frac{1}{2} \times \frac{2}{3} = ?$ Does the order matter? Are parentheses needed?

   b. $3\frac{1}{4} \times 2\frac{1}{2} = ?$ Are parentheses needed?

   c. $3.1416 \times 2.5 = ?$ Does the order matter?

4. Dividing

a. $2.5 \div \frac{1}{2} = ?$ Are parentheses needed? Does the order matter?

b. $3\frac{1}{4} \div 2\frac{1}{2} = ?$ Are parentheses needed?

c. $17.2 \div 7.3 = ?$ Are parentheses needed? What's the answer rounded to 2 decimal places to the right of the decimal point?

5. Multiply 102.506×34.9.

First estimate the answer. You might do this by choosing a whole number close to 102.506 and a whole number close to 34.9. Multiply out the two whole numbers to get your estimate. Then use the calculator to get the exact answer. Is your calculator answer fairly close (within 100) to your estimate?

SUMMARY

You can use a calculator to add, subtract, multiply, and divide:

> whole numbers
> fractions
> mixed numbers
> decimals

Always clear your calculator before you begin a problem.

After you enter a problem, press the = key and look for the answer (a decimal number) in the display window.

To enter a fraction in your calculator, first enter the numerator (top number), then the division sign ($\div$) and finally the denominator (bottom number). Press the equal (=) key to find your answer in the display window.

The **order** in which you enter numbers in your calculator **doesn't matter** when you are **adding** or **multiplying** numbers.

The order in which you enter the numbers in your calculator **does make a difference** when you are doing these things:

> subtracting
> dividing
> entering fractions
> entering mixed numbers

When you divide a fraction by a fraction, enclose the second fraction in parentheses as you carry out the operation.

When you subtract, multiply, or divide mixed numbers, surround each mixed number with parentheses as you enter it into the calculator. For instance, enter $3\frac{1}{4}$ as $(3 + 1 \div 4)$.

Always enter the numbers and operations ($+$, $-$, $\times$, or $\div$) in the same order as they are written in the problem (reading from left to right).

PRACTICING THE SKILLS

Laboratory Activity

Use the mathematics skills you have learned to complete the following activity.

Activity   **Scaled measurements**

Equipment   Ruler
Small objects (provided by teacher)
Calculator

Given   Technicians and skilled workers frequently need to make and interpret simple drawings or sketches. The drawings occasionally can be made full-scale, but more often are scaled up or scaled down to fit the page.

Find   The scaled-up and/or scaled-down lengths of variously measured dimensions.

Procedure   **a.** Your teacher will provide you with one or more objects to draw. Note that simple drawings will suffice for this activity. The important part is the measurements.

(Instead of three-dimensional objects, your teacher may suggest you measure and make a scaled drawing of the top view of the drilling jig shown at the end of this activity.)

b. Discuss in your lab group the different dimensions to be measured for your drawing. These dimensions might be lengths, widths, diameters, heights, and so on. You may want to use masking tape to attach your measurements directly to the object's dimensions. Make a data table, like the example shown below, to record your measurements.

Dimension	Length (inches)
Length A	
Length B	
Height	
⋮	⋮

c. Measure each dimension identified by your group. Record the value of your measurement to the finest division indicated on your ruler (for example, $\frac{1}{16}$ in. or $\frac{1}{64}$ in.).

d. Your instructor will assign you a scale amount such as ¼ or ⅝. Add a third column to your data table to record the values of your scaled measurements. For each of your measurements, calculate the scaled measurement by multiplying (or dividing—however your teacher instructs) your measurement value by the scale amount.

e. Use your column of scaled measurements to construct a scaled drawing of your object. Be sure to label the actual dimensions on your drawing—not the scaled values. (A standard approach for technical drawings is to separate the drawing into at least three parts: a front view, a side view, and a top view. You may find this a simpler approach than a perspective drawing.)

Wrap-up

a. Compare your object and its scaled drawing with the other groups in the class. What generalization can you make about the effect of the scale value on the size of the drawing?

b. When multiplying your measurements by the scale value, which did you find easier: multiplying fractions or multiplying decimals?

c. Did you find the calculator made your work easier? Or were you able to perform most of the calculations without using the calculator?

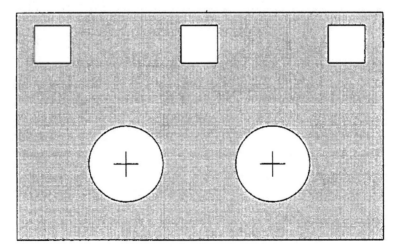

Optional "object" to measure

STUDENT EXERCISES

You can solve the exercises that follow by applying the mathematics skills you've learned. The problems described here are those you may meet in the world of work.

Note: Wherever possible, use your calculator to solve the problems that require numerical answers.

EXERCISE 1: A twenty-gallon gas tank is filled before starting a job. After a few hours of driving, the fuel gauge shows that you have used one-fourth of the tank of gas.

a. If the gauge is accurate, how many gallons of gas have been used?

b. How many gallons are left in the tank?

EXERCISE 2: The cashier rings up your purchases of $3.29 and $7.59, and adds sales tax of $0.54.

a. What is the total of your purchases and tax?

b. How much change should you receive from a twenty-dollar bill?

EXERCISE 3: Approximately 60 gallons of water are used each day by each person in the United States.

a. Using this figure, determine how much water is needed each day for a workshift of 600 people.

b. How many gallons of water are needed each day for the population of a city of 33,000?

EXERCISE 4: A warehouse has a total of 480 bays. Three pallets can be stacked in each bay, and each pallet can hold 60 cartons.

a. How many pallets is the warehouse able to store?

b. How many cartons is this?

c. The warehouse manager reports that the warehouse is about three-fourths full. About how many cartons are in the warehouse?

EXERCISE 5: After doing some tune-up work on a van, you total up the cost of the parts and materials used. You installed a clean oil filter that cost $4.70, 5 quarts of oil costing $1.10 per quart, 6 spark plugs that cost $2.47 each, and a distributor tune-up kit costing $7.95.

   a. What is the cost of the oil?

   b. What is the cost of the spark plugs?

   c. What is the total cost of parts?

EXERCISE 6: Employees at Makemfast Industries record their time-card data in units of "one-tenth hours." Mary recorded on her time card the following entries: 3.1 hours on job number 1653, 2.2 hours on job number 1731, 1.4 hours on job number 2236, 0.9 hour for lunch and breaks, and 0.4 hour of idle time.

   a. How many minutes are in one-tenth of an hour?

   b. How many total hours does Mary record on her time card?

   c. Mary's supervisor tries to keep her schedule so that her idle time is not more than $\frac{1}{20}$ of her total hours. Was Mary idle more than $\frac{1}{20}$ of her total hours this day?

EXERCISE 7: The total operating cost of a 40-passenger airline flight between two cities is $10,415. The airfare on this flight for each passenger is $360.

   a. How much would the airline receive in fares from a full load of passengers?

   b. What is the smallest number of passengers the flight could sell tickets for and still meet the operating expenses of the flight?

EXERCISE 8: A customer pays $8.00 as a down payment on a stereo system, and agrees to pay $8.75 monthly installments for the next 12 months.

   a. What is the total cost of the stereo system to the customer?

b. The stereo system was priced at $99. How much more did it cost the customer to buy the stereo system on an installment plan?

EXERCISE 9: Bill currently is working at a job where he earns $7.54 per hour, and works 40 hours each week. He has an opportunity for a promotion. The new assignment would be a salary position that pays $17,000 per year.

a. Assuming that Bill gets paid for 52 weeks at his present job (no overtime), how much does he earn a year?

b. How does this compare to the salary offer?

EXERCISE 10: You are comparing the cost of apartment rent to the cost of renting a duplex. The apartment owner furnishes all the utilities and charges a rent of $450 per month. The duplex you are considering will cost $375 per month, but you must pay the utility bills. The occupants of the other half of the duplex tell you that their monthly bills run from $40 to $80 for electricity and $10 to $20 for water.

a. Assuming your utilities would be similar to the information above, what would be the maximum you would expect your utility bills to reach per month? What would be the minimum?

b. For a month with the maximum utility bills, what would be the total cost of rent and utilities? How does this compare to the apartment rent?

c. Assume the minimum utility cost applies for half the year, and the maximum applies for the other half. What would be the total cost of the duplex rent and utilities for a year? How does this compare to the apartment rent for a year?

EXERCISE 11: The major diameter (or outside diameter) of a screw is 0.625" and the minor diameter (or inside diameter) is 0.5568" (as shown below).

a. What is the depth of the screw thread?

b. Does your answer change if there are twice as many threads per inch as that shown in the drawing?

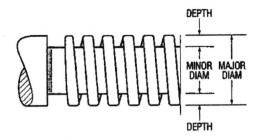

DEPTH

MINOR DIAM   MAJOR DIAM

DEPTH

EXERCISE 12: In a parallel circuit, the total circuit current equals the sum of the individual currents. A check of the current drain in a parallel kitchen circuit shows that, when in use, the refrigerator draws 3.27 amps, the electric iron draws 4.12 amps, the toaster draws 8.75 amps, and the fluorescent lights draw 0.53 amp.

a. What would be the total current drawn from this circuit if all the items were in use simultaneously?

b. Suppose the owner attaches a device that reduces the current the refrigerator uses by $\frac{1}{10}$. What will the new total current be?

EXERCISE 13: You can compute the average speed of travel by dividing distance traveled by the time needed to travel that distance. Use the distance from your home to the school in miles and approximately how long it takes you (in hours) to get to school each morning. Determine your average speed when traveling to school. (Round the final answer to 2 decimal places.)

(Hint: Convert minutes to hours by dividing the minutes by 60.)

EXERCISE 14: The volume of a typical classroom is about 8000 cubic feet.

a. If air flows through the main cooling/heating duct into the classroom at 96 cubic feet of air each minute, find out how many minutes are required to completely exchange the air in the classroom. (Round the final answer to 2 decimal places.)

b. Does it take the same amount of time if the room is full of people?

EXERCISE 15: During the course of working on a wiring job, an electrician checks out the following cable stock from the storeroom: 5 reels, 3 reels, 1 reel, 3 reels, and 4 reels. At the end of the job he returns to the storeroom 1 full reel and a partial reel with 20 feet remaining.

a. How many reels did the electrician check out from the storeroom?

b. How many feet of cable were checked out from the storeroom if each reel has 50 feet of wire?

c. How many feet of cable did the electrician use on the job?

EXERCISE 16: With a complete turn, a screw advances a distance equal to the "pitch."

a. If the pitch of a #8 screw is $\frac{1}{32}$ inch, how far will the screw advance if it is tightened 8.5 turns? (Express your answer in decimal inches, rounded to 3 decimal places.)

b. What if it is a larger screw, for example a #10 screw, with the same pitch?

EXERCISE 17: A machined part has a length of $12\frac{29}{32}$ inches. It will have two holes with $\frac{3}{4}$" diameters, with centers $2\frac{7}{16}$" from each end, as shown below. (Round the final answers to 3 decimal places.)

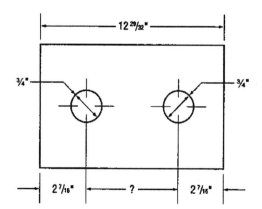

a. How far apart must the hole centers be in the finished piece?

b. How far apart must the centers be if the holes have to be enlarged to 1" diameter?

EXERCISE 18:   A 6000-pound casting of manganese bronze alloy is being made. The composition for manganese bronze is $^{11}/_{20}$ copper, $^2/_5$ zinc, $^3/_{100}$ manganese, $^1/_{125}$ tin, $^1/_{250}$ lead, and $^1/_{125}$ other impurities.

a. Find the number of pounds for each metal in the casting, and the allowance for impurities.

b. Should the fractions add up to one? Do they?

EXERCISE 19:   The bimetallic element of a thermostat is made of a strip of brass seventy-three thousandths of an inch thick in contact with a strip of iron that is one hundred twenty-five thousandths of an inch thick.

a. What is the total thickness of the bimetallic element?

b. Frequently a thousandth of an inch is referred to as a mil. What is the total thickness of the element in mils?

EXERCISE 20:   A forklift rated at 2000 pounds is used to load crates of machine parts weighing 680 pounds apiece.

a. How many crates can the forklift lift at one time without exceeding the rated maximum?

b. How many trips would be needed to move 15 crates?

Chapter 2

Naming Numbers in Different Ways

How to use your calculator to work with
fractions, decimals, and percents

Prerequisite

This chapter builds on the skills taught in Chapter 1—*Getting to Know Your Calculator.* It is the second of three preparatory chapters for **CORD Workforce Mathematics 1.** You will need a scientific calculator to complete this chapter.

To Master This Chapter

Read the text and answer all the questions. Complete the assigned problems and activity. Work the problems on the chapter test at a satisfactory level.

Chapter Objectives

Working through this chapter helps you learn how to:

1. Change percents to decimals.

2. Change decimals to percents.

3. Use a calculator to change fractions to decimals.

4. Change decimals from your calculator to fractions.

5. Solve problems that contain information in the form of fractions, decimals, or percents.

LEARNING THE SKILLS

INTRODUCTION

If you looked at a newspaper or magazine, listened to the radio, or watched TV today, you almost certainly came across the word "percent" or the symbol %.

Every time you buy a hamburger or gasoline, you work with decimal numbers.

When you share a pizza, or split the cost of a tape with your sister or brother, you work with fractions.

Fractions, decimals, and percents are different ways to name numbers.

These numbers look quite different. Do they have different values?

$$\frac{1}{2} \qquad 50\% \qquad 0.5 \qquad \text{one-half}$$

This chapter helps you understand different ways to name a number. It also shows you how to change from one kind of number to another when you need to.

You'll learn how to change from a percent (such as 75%) to a decimal (0.75) or to a fraction ($\frac{75}{100}$ or $\frac{3}{4}$). Or, going the other way, you'll learn how to change from a fraction (say $\frac{4}{10}$) to the decimal form (0.40) or to a percent (40%). In most cases, you'll be able to use your calculator to work with these numbers.

You may prefer to work with decimal numbers on your calculator. Some people are more comfortable with fractions and prefer to use that kind of number form. Certain problems use the % (or percent) form of a number.

WORKING WITH PERCENTS

You probably have read signs that said "50% Off." Or you've heard an ad on TV that claimed "93% prefer our product." Have you ever thought about what the word "percent" (or the symbol %) means?

To understand the word "percent," let's break it apart and think about what the separate words "per" and "cent" mean.

What does "cent" mean?

Have you ever heard the expression "I don't have a cent to my name?" In this expression the word cent refers to a unit of money. We all know that a dollar contains 100 cents. Therefore, a **cent** must represent ¹/₁₀₀ of a dollar. Likewise, cent appears in the word **cent**ury. So cent must also mean 100.

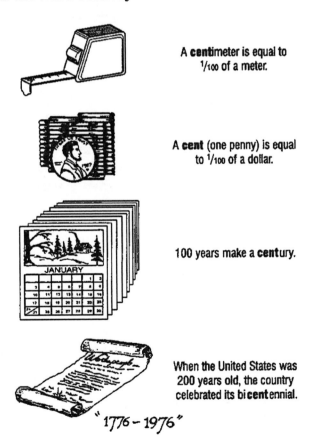

A **cent**imeter is equal to
¹/₁₀₀ of a meter.

A **cent** (one penny) is equal
to ¹/₁₀₀ of a dollar.

100 years make a **cent**ury.

When the United States was
200 years old, the country
celebrated its bi**cent**ennial.

"1776 – 1976"

Figure 1
Words with "cent"

The word "cent" comes from the Latin name for the phrase "one hundred." The word "cent" is related to the number 100. Depending on how it's used, it can mean either 100 or ¹⁄₁₀₀. In the word percent, "cent" means 100.

What does "per" mean?

If "cent" in percent means one hundred, what does **"per"** mean? What does it mean to say that a car is going "30 miles *per* hour?" What does it mean to say that a savings account pays five percent interest?

- Thirty miles **per** hour means that the car travels 30 miles *in each* hour.

- Five **percent** interest means that 5 dollars are earned *for each* 100 dollars in the account.

The word **"per"** stands for several simple words such as **in each, for each, out of each,** and so on.

Now that you know what the two words that make up "per cent" mean, let's put them back together. We usually write "percent" or % when we talk about how many parts for each hundred parts.

Percent means how many parts out of each hundred parts.

A savings account that pays 5 per*cent* interest will pay you $5 **for each** $100 you have in your account. What does it mean if a store advertises "30 **percent** off " all items in the store? It means that you can save $30 **out of each** $100 you spend or 30 cents **out of each** 100 cents (or dollar) you spend.

If a plant-food mixture is 75 percent water, how many ounces out of each 100 pints of mixture are water? How many ounces will be pure plant food? Use Figure 2 to help you find the answer.

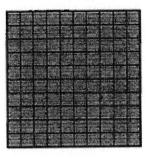
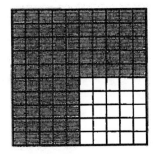

THE WHOLE
100 PARTS OUT OF 100 PARTS

75% OF THE WHOLE
75 PARTS OUT OF 100 PARTS

Figure 2
Representing seventy-five percent

Now that you know what the two words that make up
"percent" mean, let's put them back together. We usually
write "percent" (or %) when we talk about how many parts
for each hundred parts.

 **Percent means how many parts out of each hundred
parts.**

What kind of number is percent?

Look at this list. Each item names something.

> 50 cents
> 7 pounds of apples
> 5 aspirin
> 20 sacks of feed
> 9 roofing nails
> 15 percent

If someone sent you to the store to buy everything on the list,
could you find each item and bring it back? Why not?
Clearly, the last item—a percent—is not a thing. We have to
know "15 percent of what?" before "15 percent" makes sense.
You can draw 15 squares, or 15 circles, or 15 lines, but you
can't draw "15 percent."

 Where would you see the word percent when you read a
newspaper or walk by some stores? When do you use the
word percent? Write a list of the ways you see or use the
word percent.

Ways to use percent

Do you leave a tip when you eat in a restaurant? If so, how much? Also, do you pay sales tax? How much? Figure 3 shows a guest check that lists both the tip and the sales tax. (Would you rather pay the tip before or after the tax is figured?)

Both tips and sales tax are expressed as percents of the total bill or the total amount of money spent.

Percents can be expressed easily as decimals because they are based on 100. Your calculator is helpful because it uses decimals.

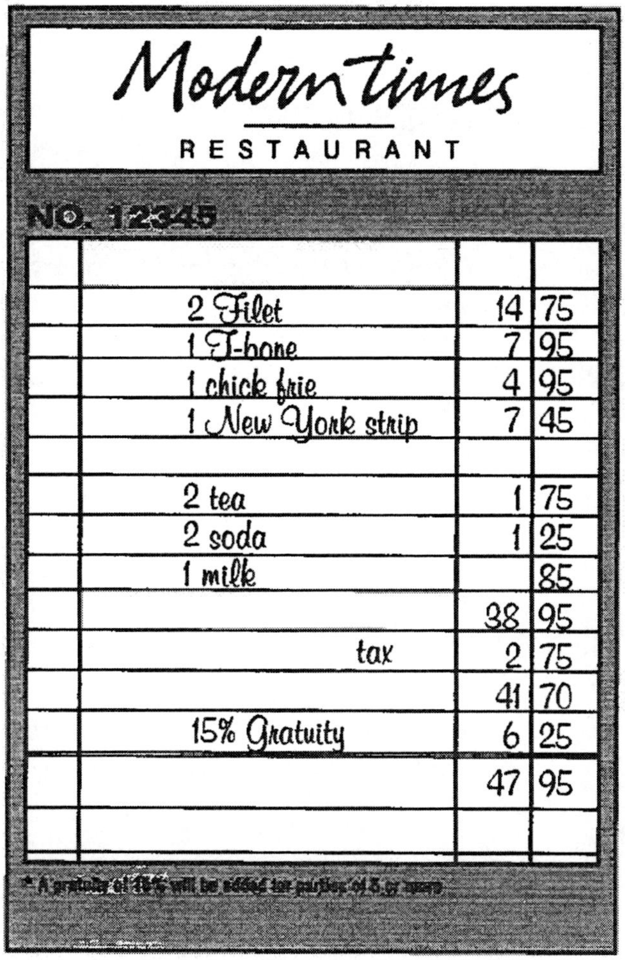

Modern times

RESTAURANT

NO. 12345

	2 Filet	14	75
	1 T-bone	7	95
	1 chick frie	4	95
	1 New York strip	7	45
	2 tea	1	75
	2 soda	1	25
	1 milk		85
		38	95
	tax	2	75
		41	70
	15% Gratuity	6	25
		47	95

* A gratuity of 15% will be added for parties of 5 or more

Figure 3
Tip and sales tax on a meal

CHANGING PERCENTS TO DECIMALS

Think about the tip you pay for a meal as an example. In many places, 15% (fifteen percent) is a usual amount to tip. The word "per" is a clue just like the slash (/) mark in a fraction. *Per* means ÷ or "divided by," so *percent* means "divided by 100." As an example, fifteen percent (15%) means ¹⁵⁄₁₀₀ or 15 ÷ 100.

Fifteen percent (15%) means ¹⁵⁄₁₀₀ or 15 ÷ 100. Enter this fraction into your calculator to see 15% written as a decimal number.

When you divide 15 by 100, your calculator displays 0.15. (Your calculator may not show the 0 before the decimal point, but we put it in so you will see the decimal point more clearly.) Your calculator tells you that 15% is the same as fifteen-hundredths.

To change a percent to a decimal number, write or think of the percent as a fraction (a number divided by 100) and then enter the fraction into your calculator.

Study Activity: Use your calculator to change these percents to decimal numbers.

> 10%
>
> 25%
>
> 85%
>
> 99%
>
> 125%

What happened with that last percent? How was your answer to 125% different from the others? Why?

Percents more than 100%

One hundred twenty-five percent (125%) is ¹²⁵⁄₁₀₀ or one hundred twenty-five hundredths.

You know that $^{100}/_{100}$ is another name for the number 1.
Because $^{125}/_{100}$ is more than $^{100}/_{100}$, you can see that $^{125}/_{100}$ has
to be more than 1. Figure 4 shows this.

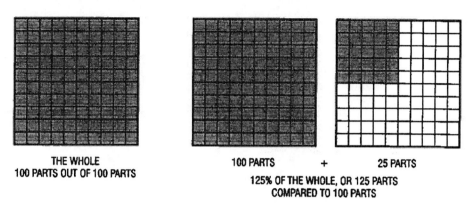

THE WHOLE
100 PARTS OUT OF 100 PARTS

100 PARTS + 25 PARTS

125% OF THE WHOLE, OR 125 PARTS
COMPARED TO 100 PARTS

Figure 4
Percents more than 100%

Study Activity: Use your calculator to change these percents to decimal
numbers.

150%

45%

100%

15%

275%

3%

Now look at your results and answer these questions.

1. If a percent is *less* than 100%, what will it look like as a
decimal number? Where will the decimal point be?

2. If a percent is *more* than 100%, what will it look like as a
decimal number? Where will the decimal point be?

What pattern did you notice? Choose some percent numbers
yourself and change them to decimal numbers to double-check
your answers to the two questions.

Percents to decimals (shortcut)

You now have practiced changing percents to decimal numbers by first writing the percent in its fraction form and then dividing the numerator by the denominator (which is always 100). Have you noticed a pattern that helps you quickly change a percent to a decimal number? Write this sentence on your paper and fill in the blanks.

To change a percent to a decimal number, remove the _____ and move the decimal point _____ places to the _____.

If you remember that 1.0 (or $^{100}/_{100}$) is 100% and 0.50 (or $^{50}/_{100}$) is 50%, you can use these two examples to check which way to move the decimal point. Remember that for a whole number like 10, 1, or 45, the decimal point is just to the right of the last digit even if it is not shown. So, for a number like 45%, you know that the decimal point is just after the 5, even though "45" is written without it.

Study Activity: Change these percents to decimal numbers using the shortcut method.

    10%

    1%

    100%

    0.1%

    45%

    125%

    63.3%

    5%

CHANGING DECIMALS TO PERCENTS

How do you change a decimal number to a percent?

Think about the number 0.15. What is its name as a percent? That is, 0.15 = what %?

The decimal number 0.15 has <u>two</u> places to the right of the decimal point. Figure 5 shows the name of each decimal place.

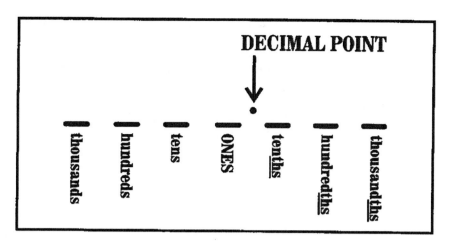

Figure 5
Decimal place names

Numbers that end in the **second place** to the right of the decimal point name the decimal place to **hundredths.**

$$0.15 = {}^{15}\!/_{100}$$

But ${}^{15}\!/_{100}$ is 15 divided by 100, which can be written as 15%.

So now we have

$$0.15 = {}^{15}\!/_{100} = 15\%$$

Study Activity: Change these decimal numbers to fractions and then change the fractions to percents.

0.25
0.75
0.40
0.62

Here is another way to think about changing a decimal number to a percent.

Think about the decimal number 0.15 again. We want to rename it as a percent. Two facts help you make this change easily: One, we can multiply any number by the number one (1) without changing its value. Two, 100% is another name for 1.

To change 0.15 to a percent, multiply it by 100%. This does not change its value because 100% is another name for 1.

$$0.15 = 0.15 \times 100\% = (0.15 \times 100)\% = 15\%$$

Study Activity: Change each of these decimal numbers to a percent by multiplying by 100%.

> 0.12
>
> 0.45
>
> 1.35
>
> 1.00
>
> 6.00
>
> 0.125
>
> 0.01
>
> 0.5

Look at your answers. Can you see a pattern that helps you quickly multiply by 100 even without a calculator? Does the pattern hold true for the numbers given below?

Decimal		Percent
0.50	is	50%
0.5	is	50%
1.5	is	150%
0.15	is	15%
0.005	is	0.5%
3 (or 3.00)	is	300%
0.3	is	30%
0.03	is	3%
0.003	is	0.3%
0.0003	is	0.03%

Steps for changing decimals to percents

On your paper, write the following four steps for changing any decimal number to a percent. Fill in the blanks as you write.

To change any decimal number to a percent:

1. If the decimal number does not have a decimal point, write one at the end—to the right of the last number.

2. Insert zeros at the end (to the right) until the number has at least _____ decimal places.

3. Rewrite the number by moving the decimal point _____ places to the _____ and adding a percent sign.

4. If there is no digit in front of the decimal point, put a 0 there so the decimal point won't get lost.

If you understand how to work with zeros and decimal points, these four steps reduce to just one step:

To change a decimal number to a percent, move the decimal point two places to the right and add the % sign.

Notice that this is just the opposite of the shortcut that changes a percent to a decimal number.

Comparing decimals, fractions, and percents

Money is a common item that makes it possible for us to compare decimal names, fraction names, and percent names.

Our dollar is divided into 100 pennies. One penny ($0.01 or 1 cent) is ¹⁄₁₀₀ of a dollar or 1% of a dollar.

If you think about 0.75 as seventy-five cents ($0.75), you can see that it is the same as ⁷⁵⁄₁₀₀ (of a dollar) or 75% (of one dollar).

Figure 6 lists different names for 0.75 and illustrates its value with pennies.

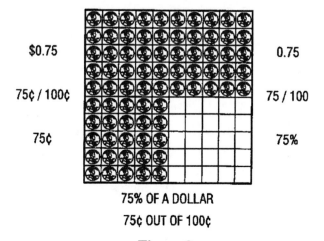

$0.75   0.75

75¢ / 100¢   75 / 100

75¢   75%

75% OF A DOLLAR

75¢ OUT OF 100¢

Figure 6
Different names for the decimal number 0.75

CHANGING DECIMALS TO FRACTIONS

Sometimes the decimal answer you get is not in the form you want. You may want to change the decimal answer to a simple fraction—or to a mixed number. How do you change a decimal to a fraction?

Changing decimals to simple fractions

Here's an example of changing a decimal number obtained with a calculator to a mixed number. The example also shows how to change the fraction part of the mixed number to a simpler fraction.

Example 1:
Calculating molding needs

Marie has torn up the carpet in a room and measured how much molding she needs to put down over the gap where the floor meets the wall. She needs pieces that are these lengths: 8¾ ft, 6½ ft, 2⅓ ft, 2⅝ ft, 1⅔ ft, and 5⅜ ft. She uses her calculator to add these, and her calculator tells her that she needs 27.25 feet of molding.

She knows, however, that the molding usually is bought in feet and fractions of a foot. How can she change 27.25 feet into a mixed number (made up of a whole number and a fraction)? She knows she wants 27 feet plus some fraction of a foot. To what fraction is 0.25 equal?

Marie remembers that 0.25 is ²⁵⁄₁₀₀. Therefore, she could write the mixed number as 27²⁵⁄₁₀₀. But she thinks she can write ²⁵⁄₁₀₀ in a simpler form. So she "reduces" the fraction ²⁵⁄₁₀₀ by dividing both the numerator (top number) and the denominator (bottom number) of the fraction by 25, as follows:

$$\frac{25}{100} = \frac{25 \div 25}{100 \div 25} = \frac{1}{4}$$

This gives her ¼. Now she can write the mixed number as 27¼. She can then go to the lumber store and buy 27 and ¼ feet of molding. (She may have to buy 28 feet if the molding is sold only by the foot.)

If Marie had recognized right away that 0.25 is the same as ¼ she would have been able to change from a decimal to a mixed number immediately. See Figure 7.

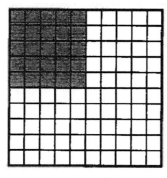
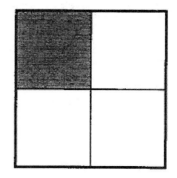

25% OF THE WHOLE
($^{25}/_{100}$ OR 25 PARTS OUT OF 100)

ONE-FOURTH OF THE WHOLE
(¼ OR ONE PART OUT OF FOUR PARTS)

Figure 7
Changing a decimal to a fraction

In the next section you'll make a chart that helps you change a decimal to a fraction.

Eleven common fractions

In most practical situations, there are only a few fractions that we use as we measure most things. Let's make a chart so we can easily change decimal answers from the calculator into these common fractions. This also will make it easy to change common fractions to decimals or percents.

Study Activity:

Copy this list of proper fractions with denominators from two to ten onto your own paper. (Recall that a proper fraction always has a number in the numerator that is less than the number in the denominator, such as the fraction ⅔.)

½
⅓   ⅔
¼   ²⁄₄   ¾
⅕   ⅖   ⅗   ⅘
⅙   ²⁄₆   ³⁄₆   ⁴⁄₆   ⅚

Skip the sevenths—nobody measures in sevenths!

⅛   ²⁄₈   ⅜   ⁴⁄₈   ⅝   ⁶⁄₈   ⅞

Skip the ninths too!

⅒   ²⁄₁₀   ³⁄₁₀   and so on.

We skipped sevenths and ninths because they don't occur very often as we work real-world problems.

How can we convert tenths into decimals or percents? Take ⁷⁄₁₀ as an example. This is 0.7 (or 0.70) as a decimal and 70% as a percent. Tenths are so easy to convert that we can leave them out of our chart.

What about fifths? To what fraction does ²⁄₁₀ reduce? Did you get ⅕? Can you show how ²⁄₁₀ reduces to ⅕?

The fraction ⅖ can be changed to tenths by multiplying both the numerator and denominator of the fraction by 2 (the opposite of reducing the fraction).

$$\frac{2}{5} = \frac{2 \times 2}{5 \times 2} = \frac{4}{10}$$

This changes ⅖ to ⁴⁄₁₀, which is 0.4 or 40% (40 percent). When we change fractions in fifths to fractions in tenths or hundredths, they become easier to change to decimals. Figure 8 shows graphically that ²⁄₁₀ = ⅕, ⁴⁄₁₀ = ⅖, ⁶⁄₁₀ = ⅗, and ⁸⁄₁₀ = ⅘.

Look at the chart you just made. Circle all the fractions that have 5 as denominators, and circle those that have 10 as denominators. You know an easy way to convert those. Now look at the chart again.

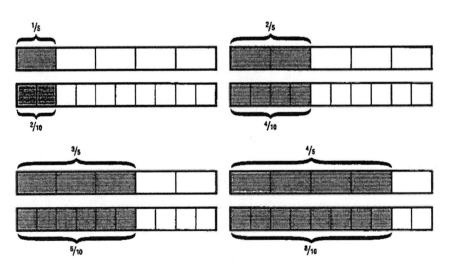

EXAMPLE: $\frac{2}{5} = \frac{2 \times 2}{5 \times 2} = \frac{4}{10} = 0.4 = 40\%$

Figure 8
Changing fifths to tenths

How about ²⁄₄? Can you reduce that fraction so that it equals another one in the chart? Circle ²⁄₄ because it is the same as ½.

$$\frac{2}{4} = \frac{2 \div 2}{4 \div 2} = \frac{1}{2}$$

Circle any of the sixths and eighths that you can reduce.

How many **UN**circled fractions do you have left on your chart? If you have more than eleven, look again to see if you can reduce any of them.

≈ The eleven fractions left uncircled are the ones that will be part of the chart. You should have: ½, ⅓, ⅔, ¼, ¾, ⅙, ⅚, ⅛, ⅜, ⅝, ⅞. The circled fractions do not need to be in the chart; some of them are easy to convert to decimals. Other fractions (such as the ninths) are not common enough to worry about. The uncircled ones are the common fractions that you often will need to change into decimals, or to change from decimals back into fractions. Now you are ready to complete the chart for eleven common fractions.

Study Activity: Copy the chart shown below in Figure 9 on your paper. Use your calculator to find the decimal value for each fraction. (Remember, for example, "½" means 1 ÷ 2.) Write the decimal value in the second column in the chart. Then, fill in the percent column.

Fraction	Decimal	Percent
½		
⅓		
⅔		
¼		
¾		
⅙		
⅚		
⅛		
⅜		
⅝		
⅞		

Figure 9
Chart for eleven common fractions

Decimals that go on forever

When you put the fractions in Figure 9 in your calculator, some of the decimal answers you get may look a little strange. For instance, ⅓ gives 0.3333333 (your calculator may show a different number of threes). The fraction ⅓ names an **unending repeating** decimal; the decimal goes on forever. That is because 3 will never divide evenly into 1 even if you keep dividing forever!

There are different ways to indicate that the 3 repeats forever (for example, 0.333..., or 0.3$\overline{3}$). Most of the time we just round the number to hundredths, so ⅓ becomes approximately 0.33 as a decimal. That decimal is ³³⁄₁₀₀ or 33%, so ⅓ is approximately 33%. We can write ⅓ exactly as a percent if we use a fraction. This means that ⅓ is exactly 33⅓ percent.

Write 33⅓% in your chart as the percent for ⅓.

What do you get when you enter the fraction ⅔ into your calculator? Again, the 6s will continue forever. If you want to round to the hundredths place, ⅔ is approximately 0.67 or 67 percent. More precisely, ⅔ is exactly 66⅔%.

Write 66⅔% in your chart as the percent for ⅔.

The decimal names for ⅙ and ⅚ are similar. Remember that 0.333333 (unending and repeating) is exactly ⅓ and 0.666666 (unending and repeating) is exactly ⅔, and use that information to write the decimal and percent names for ⅙ and ⅚ in the chart.

Completing the chart

What happens with eighths? All of the fractions with eight as the denominator come out evenly with three decimal places. Use your calculator to divide ⅛, ⅜, ⅝, and ⅞ and fill in their decimal and percent names.

Complete any blank places in your chart and check it.

Now you can use the chart to change fractions to decimals or percents. You can also use it to change decimals or percents to fractions.

Practice in changing decimals to fractions

Use the chart, your calculator, and what you know about fractions, percents, and decimals to help you answer these questions.

Study Activity: **a.** Bill used his calculator to find out that he needed 3.625 feet of brass rod. Change the decimal number shown on Bill's calculator to a mixed number. (Recall that a mixed number is a combination of a whole number and a fraction—such as 2½.)

b. Sue measured the length and width of pieces for a custom-made picture frame. She found that she needed these pieces:

two pieces each 10⅜ inches long
two pieces each 15¾ inches long

Add these lengths with your calculator. What *decimal* answer did you get?

Use the chart to change this decimal answer to a *mixed number*.

c. If ⅗ of the people in a survey of the "best" soap powders picked Brand X, what *percent* of the people chose Brand X?

d. Write ⅔ as a *percent* (exactly).

e. Write 70% as a *fraction*.

f. Write 23.83 as a *mixed number* (approximately).

g. What *fraction* is 0.6667 (approximately)?

h. You measure several pieces of rope and add their lengths with your calculator. You find that you need 9.75 feet of rope overall. What *mixed number* would you use to say how much rope you want to buy?

A drill size example

Figure 10 shows part of a pocket-size plastic card that lists drill size information. People who work with tools use this card to see what drill size (measured in fractions of an inch or drill size numbers) will make what size hole (measured in decimal numbers).

DRILL SIZE								
Number	Fraction	Decimal	Metric (mm)		Number	Fraction	Decimal	Metric (mm)
80		0.0135	0.3412		46		0.0810	2.0574
79		0.0145	0.3788		45		0.0820	2.0828
—	1/64	0.0156	0.3969		44		0.0860	2.1844
78		0.0160	0.4064		43		0.0890	2.2606
77		0.0180	0.4572		42		0.0935	2.3622
76		0.0200	0.5080		—	3/32	0.0937	2.3812
75		0.0210	0.5334		41		0.0960	2.4384
74		0.0225	0.5631		40		0.0980	2.4892
73		0.0240	0.6096		39		0.0995	2.5377
72		0.0250	0.6350		38		0.1015	2.5908
71		0.0260	0.6604		37		0.1040	2.6416
70		0.0280	0.7112		36		0.1065	2.6924
69		0.0292	0.7483		—	7/64	0.1094	2.7781
68		0.0310	0.7874		35		0.1100	2.7490
—	1/32	0.0312	0.7937		34		0.1110	2.8194
67		0.0320	0.8128		33		0.1130	2.8702
66		0.0330	0.8382		32		0.1160	2.9464
65		0.0350	0.8890		31		0.1200	3.0480
64		0.0360	0.9144		—	1/8	0.1250	3.1750
63		0.0370	0.9398					
62		0.0380	0.9652		30		0.1285	3.2766
61		0.0390	0.9906		29		0.1360	3.4544
60		0.0400	1.0160		28		0.1405	3.5560
59		0.0410	1.0414		—	9/64	0.1406	3.5719
58		0.0420	1.0668		27		0.1440	3.6576
57		0.0430	1.0922		26		0.1470	3.7338
56		0.0465	1.1684		25		0.1495	3.7886
—	3/64	0.0469	1.1906		24		0.1520	3.8608
55		0.0520	1.3208		23		0.1540	3.9116
54		0.0550	1.3970		—	5/32	0.1562	3.9687
53		0.0595	1.5122		22		0.1570	3.9678
—	1/16	0.0625	1.5875		21		0.1590	4.0386
52		0.0635	1.6002		20		0.1610	4.0894
51		0.0670	1.7018		19		0.1660	4.2164
50		0.0700	1.7780		18		0.1695	4.3180
49		0.0730	1.8542		—	11/64	0.1719	4.3656
48		0.0760	1.9304		17		0.1730	4.3942
—	5/64	0.0781	1.9844		16		0.1770	4.4958
47		0.0785	2.0001		15		0.1800	4.5720

Figure 10
Part of drill size chart

Plumbers, carpenters, machinists, and other craftspersons use fractions of an inch to measure the size of a drill bit. These fractional sizes are in the second column of each section of the card. Some workers also use letters of the alphabet and drill size numbers from 1 to 80 to measure the size of a drill bit. These letters and numbers are in the first column of each card section.

The third column shows the sizes of the holes made by the drill bits as decimal numbers in inches. These hole sizes are in decimal numbers, rounded to the nearest ten-thousandth of an inch (four places to the right of the decimal point). For example, the card tells you that a #68 drill bit has a diameter of 0.0310 inch (just a tiny bit smaller than $\frac{1}{32}$ inch) or a diameter of 0.7874 mm.

The fourth column gives the same diameter in metric measure—to the nearest ten-thousandth of a meter or millimeter (mm).

Study Activity: Use the chart in Figure 10 to answer these questions. Write the answers on a separate sheet of paper.

a. Maggie needs to attach some piping to a piece of equipment. The plans indicate that a hole needs to be 0.0320 inch in diameter. What size drill bit should she use?

b. To drill a hole that is 0.18 inch in diameter, what size drill bit would you use?

c. You measure the width of a hole to be 0.0785 inch. What size drill bit would you use to make another hole of the same size?

d. Which proper fraction, in inches, is nearest to a measurement of 0.0785 inch?

e. A machinist needs to make a hole that is just larger than $\frac{3}{64}$ inch. What size drill bit should the machinist use?

f. The fraction $\frac{3}{32}$ is twice as big as the fraction $\frac{3}{64}$. Is the decimal equivalent for $\frac{3}{32}$ inch given in the chart twice that for $\frac{3}{64}$ inch?

g. Is a #17 drill bit twice as large as a #34 drill bit?

h. Your friend asks you to hand her a drill bit that will make a hole size just under 0.1720 inch. What size drill bit would you hand her? To what fractional value in inches is this size drill bit nearest?

SUMMARY

Percent means how many parts in each hundred parts. For example, 43 percent (43%) means that there are 43 parts in each hundred parts.

When you write a decimal fraction (with no whole number part) put a *zero* before the decimal point so the decimal point won't get lost.

To enter a fraction in your calculator, divide the numerator (top number) by the denominator (bottom number).

Numbers written as decimals—such as 31.375—have whole numbers to the left and right of the decimal point. The places to the left are ones, tens, hundreds, thousands, and so on. The places to the right are tenths, hundredths, thousandths, and so on (see below). The number 31.375 indicates that it is made up of 3 tens, 1 one, 3 tenths, 7 hundredths, and 5 thousandths.

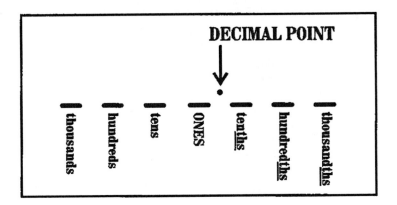

To change a percent to a decimal, remove the percent sign and move the decimal point *two* places to the *left*. For example, for the value 39%, remove the percent sign (that leaves 39) and move the decimal point (just after the 9, even though it's not shown) two places to the left. The answer is .39 or 0.39.

To change a decimal to a percent, move the decimal point *two* places to the **right** and add the % sign. For example, for the decimal 0.78, move the decimal point two places to the right to get 78. Then add the % sign to the right of the number to get 78%.

The chart given below lists the decimal and percent equivalents for eleven common fractions. If you are given one of the values listed in the chart, you can find the other two equivalent values. For example, the chart indicates that the fraction ⅛ has a decimal equivalent of 0.125 and a percent value of 12.5%. The chart also can be used to tell you that a decimal of 0.25 is equal to a fraction of ¼ or a percent of 25%.

Fraction	Decimal	Percent
½	0.5	50%
⅓	0.33 (approx)	33⅓%
⅔	0.67 (approx)	66⅔%
¼	0.25	25%
¾	0.75	75%
⅙	0.17 (approx)	16⅔%
⅚	0.83 (approx)	83⅓%
⅛	0.125	12.5% (or 12½%)
⅜	0.375	37.5% (or 37½%)
⅝	0.625	62.5% (or 62½%)
⅞	0.875	87.5% (or 87½%)

PRACTICING THE SKILLS

Laboratory Activity

Use the mathematics skills you have learned to complete the following activity.

Activity:	**Rating popcorn**
Equipment	Hot-air popcorn popper Large bowl Three brands of popcorn Calculator
Given	One way to rate popcorn is to determine which brand ends up with the fewest unpopped kernels.
Find	The best and worst of three brands of popcorn.
Procedure	**a.** Count out 100 kernels (or some such reasonable number) of one of the brands of popcorn. Pop the 100 kernels.

b. When the popping is complete, count the popped kernels. Count the unpopped kernels. Do they add to 100?

c. What fraction of the popcorn is popped? What fraction of the popcorn is unpopped?

d. What percent of the popcorn is popped? What percent of the popcorn is unpopped?

e. Repeat Steps **a** through **d** for the other two brands.

f. Which brand of popcorn had the smallest percent of unpopped kernels? Which brand had the largest percent of unpopped kernels?

g. Did your rating of the popcorn brands agree with the other groups in your class? Did your percentages agree with the other groups in your class? Is this a fair way to rate popcorn?

STUDENT EXERCISES

You can solve the exercises that follow by applying the mathematics skills you've learned.

Note: *Wherever possible, use your calculator to solve the problems that require numerical answers.*

EXERCISE 1:   Your supervisor reports that 4 workers did not come to work today because of illness.

    a. If your shift has 25 workers, what fraction of the workers did not report for work?

    b. What fraction reported for work?

    c. Express the fractions as decimals, and then as percents.

EXERCISE 2:   Suppose 7.05% of your monthly wages is withheld for social security tax, and you earn $858.76 each month.

    a. Convert 7.05% to a decimal.

    b. How much is withheld for social security tax each month? (Round to the nearest cent.)

    c. If you earn the same amount each month of the year, how much social security tax will be withheld in a twelve-month period?

    d. Will this annual amount be 7.05% of your annual earnings?

EXERCISE 3:   Marianne owns 175 shares of stock that sell for 26⅛ (dollars) per share. What is the value of Marianne's stock? (Round to the nearest cent.)

EXERCISE 4:   Kim's earnings put her in a 15% tax bracket. That means she owes the government 15% of her taxable income. She has a business opportunity that will increase her annual taxable income by $1,200.00.

    a. Express the tax-bracket percentage as a decimal.

    b. How much additional income tax can she expect to owe (assuming she will stay in the same tax bracket)?

EXERCISE 5:   A certain state requires a state sales tax of 5%, and the city adds an additional 1⅛%. (Don't round in this exercise.)

a. Change each of the percentages to a decimal.

b. Add the two decimal values. Change them back to a percentage to find the total percent tax required on purchases in this city.

c. How much total tax (state and city taxes) can a consumer expect to pay on a $72 purchase at the cash register?

EXERCISE 6:   The Imprint Advertising Company purchased 50 cartons of glass ornaments, each holding 120 ornaments, for their inventory stock. The receiving department estimated that 5% were broken at the time they arrived.

a. How many total ornaments were received?

b. Express 5% as a decimal and calculate how many ornaments were broken.

EXERCISE 7:   A high-volume photocopier is advertised as being very reliable, averaging less than 0.2 paper jams per 1000 copies when using the proper paper. A small photocopy business buys one of these machines and logs 129 paper jams during a month in which they run 382,926 copies.

a. What fraction of copies run does the manufacturer claim as the maximum number of jams? Express this fraction as a decimal.

b. What fraction of copies is the small business finding are jamming? Express this fraction as a decimal with 4 decimal places.

c. Compare the two fractions. Is the actual fraction of jams seen by the small business more or less than the advertised fraction?

EXERCISE 8:   A savings account pays 1% interest on the monthly balance. On January 1 your account has $500.00 in it. Suppose that you do not withdraw or add any more money for the entire year.

a. How much interest will be paid to your account at the end of January? What then is the total in your account?

b. How much interest will be paid to your account at the end of February? What then is the total in your account?

c. Continue this series of calculations to find out how much will be in your account at the end of December. (Round to the nearest cent.)

EXERCISE 9: A company requires a score of at least 70% on its certification exam for a certain job. In other words, you must correctly answer at least 70% of the questions that you attempt.

a. If you attempt 350 questions, and miss 28 of them, what fraction of the attempted questions have you missed? $28/350$

b. What percentage have you missed? .08

c. What percentage have you answered correctly? 92%

d. What is the most you could have missed and still qualified for certification? 105

EXERCISE 10: The instructions with the cleaner concentrate tell you to prepare a mixture of concentrate in water, one part concentrate with nine parts water. You will prepare the mix in a container that holds 64 fluid ounces of cleaning mixture.

a. If you were to prepare one batch with one fluid ounce of concentrate and nine fluid ounces of water, how many total ounces would be in the batch?

b. What fraction of the batch is concentrate?

c. What percentage of the batch is concentrate?

d. How many full batches could fit in the container?

EXERCISE 11: Brazing solder contains 51.2% copper, 48.3% zinc, 0.1% iron, and 0.4% lead.

a. Express each of the percentages as a decimal. (Show three decimal places.)

b. In a 2000-pound batch of solder, how much of each ingredient is present?

EXERCISE 12: Your coworker needs a piece of bar stock from the metal shop that is cut to a length of $16\frac{17}{64}$ inches. The supply clerk reports that the last piece available is $16\frac{1}{2}$ inches.

a. Express the desired length as a decimal, rounded to 2 decimal places.

b. Express the available length of stock as a decimal, rounded to 2 decimal places.

c. Is the available piece big enough to satisfy the required length?

EXERCISE 13: A drawing (shown below) calls for 4 pieces of $0.5" \times 0.75"$ rectangular bar stock, each 0.75" long. You will use a saw that removes $\frac{1}{8}"$ of material as it cuts (because the saw blade is nearly $\frac{1}{8}"$ wide). (Round your final answers to two decimal places.)

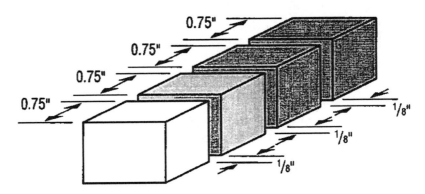

a. Use the drawing to find out what is the smallest single length of bar stock you can use to obtain the four pieces.

b. How much stock could you save by using a $\frac{1}{16}"$ saw blade?

EXERCISE 14:   A production report shows that 1726 units of a machine part were produced, and 23 units were rejected by quality control. Standard procedure requires that the production line be shut down for investigation if the reject level exceeds 2%. (Round your final answers to two decimal places.)

a. What fraction of the units produced was rejected?

b. What percentage is this?

c. Are the rejects in excess of the limit of 2%?

d. If the production line produces about 230 units per hour, about how many rejects might be tolerated during an hour before it was evident that the line was in excess of the standard?

EXERCISE 15:   When selecting the proper copper wiring to operate an electric motor, a common guideline suggests that one allow for 125% of the motor's full-load current. You have a motor with a full-load current of 15 amps.

a. Express 125% as a decimal.

b. What maximum current should you allow for when wiring for this motor?

EXERCISE 16:   The "half-life" of a particular form of radon is about 4 days. This means that after 4 days, the activity of the material—measured in counts per minute—will decrease by ½. A room containing this radon has an activity of 1800 counts per minute.

a. Express the fraction ½ as a decimal.

b. If the room is sealed off so that no radon enters or leaves, how many counts per minute would you expect after 4 days have passed?

c. After <u>another</u> four days, how many counts per minute can be expected?

d. What fraction of the original activity (counts per minute) exists after 8 days? What percentage is this?

EXERCISE 17:   Maxine is figuring out how many 2" × 6" × 8' boards she will need. She estimates that the job will require 69 boards. She has learned to allow an additional 15% (of the actual needed amount) for waste on a job's materials.

a. How many additional boards should she purchase to provide for waste?

b. How many 2" × 6" × 8' boards should Maxine buy?

c. If Maxine decides to simply buy 100 boards, what fraction is she actually allowing for waste? Is this more or less than her guideline of 15%?

EXERCISE 18:   It takes 40 minutes to machine a certain component with a high-speed steel cutter. You know that a tungsten-carbide cutter can reduce the job time by 35%.

a. How long would it take to machine one of these components using a tungsten-carbide cutter?

b. How long would it take to fill an order for 160 of these components with the steel cutter? With the tungsten-carbide cutter?

c. How much time could you save on this order with the tungsten-carbide cutter?

EXERCISE 19:   A 125-foot length of copper tubing is connected between two points along a straight line. The copper tubing is used as a transfer line that can experience temperatures from 70°F to 250°F. It is known that each foot of copper tubing increases in length by 0.00085% for each degree (1 F°) rise in temperature. Don't round in this exercise except where indicated.

a. Write 0.00085% as a decimal.

b. How much will the 125-foot copper tubing lengthen for a one-degree rise in temperature?

c. The copper tubing is 125 feet long at 70°F. How much longer will it be when the temperature changes from 70°F to 250°F?

d. What is the new length at 250°F? (Round answer to 2 decimal places.)

e. Would your answer be different if the copper tubing were not laid out along a straight line?

EXERCISE 20: A factory has three machines that each can produce about 250 parts per day for assembly. Past experience has shown that some of the production from these machines needs reworking. Records show the amount of rework to be:

Machine #	Avg Rework
#1	2%
#2	3%
#3	7%

a. How many total parts can the factory produce each day?

b. How many parts needing rework does the factory produce each day (on the average)?

c. What fraction of the factory's total production needs rework? Express this as a decimal. Express this as a percentage.

d. Someone suggests that Machine #3 be shut down completely to improve the rework percentage. If this is done, how many parts will the factory be able to produce each day? What will be the new rework percentage for the factory?

(This page is intentionally blank.)

Chapter 3

Finding Answers with
Your Calculator

How to read the clues and decode problems so you can
understand them and find the answers

| **Prerequisites** | This chapter builds on the skills taught in Chapter 1: *Getting to Know Your Calculator* and Chapter 2: *Naming Numbers in Different Ways*. It is the third of three preparatory chapters for **CORD Workforce Mathematics 1**. You will need a scientific calculator—with memory keys—to complete this chapter. |

| **To Master This Chapter** | Read the text and answer all questions. Complete the assigned activity and exercises. Work the problems on the chapter test at a satisfactory level. |

Chapter Objectives

Working through this chapter will help you to learn to:

1. Read the problem and begin to understand the situation.

2. Figure out what the problem is asking you to find.

3. Decide what math operations $(+, -, \times, \div)$ to do as you solve a problem.

4. Use your calculator to work problems that have more than one step.

LEARNING THE SKILLS

INTRODUCTION

Have you ever thought about how many ways you have to express just one idea? For instance, how do you invite a friend to have a cool drink with you? Do you say "Let's have a pop"? Or do you use the word "soda," or "soft drink," or "soda pop," or do you name a specific brand? However you say it, your friend probably understands you.

Sometimes it is not so easy to understand the idea or question in a mathematics problem. Just as there are many ways to say "soft drink," there may be four or five ways to say the same thing in mathematics. This chapter shows you some of the different ways to say the same thing in mathematics problems.

You already know that one number can have many names. In this chapter you will see the different names that mathematics operations like addition, subtraction, multiplication, and division can have.

In a mathematics book you may see lots of problems that look something like this: 7 + 19 = ? As you work at a job, the problems don't look like that! A problem at your workplace is more likely to look like this: "Find out how many of these we need to finish the job." No one tells you whether to add, subtract, multiply, or divide. You just know that you must "figure it out."

This chapter helps you decide which math operations to do, and shows you how to use your calculator to do them.

USING A STEP-BY-STEP PLAN TO SOLVE A PROBLEM

Sometimes when you read a problem, you may see the answer right away. If someone says to you, "Please hand me one more nail," you don't have to think very long to solve that problem. However, as you know, most problems are not that easy to figure out.

Treat the problem as a puzzle.

When you need to work a mathematics problem, whether it is in a textbook or on the job, it is not enough to *work* the problem and just get an answer. You need to get a *correct* answer! You can't quit when you have an answer, *any* answer. You have to find an answer that gets the job done right!

Treat the problem as a puzzle to be solved. Look for clues to help you decode the words and find the answer. What kind of clues? You already know that the *numbers* in a problem are clues. Sometimes there may be *extra* numbers in a problem—clues that you won't use. Are there other kinds of clues in a problem that tell you what to do with the numbers? As you'll see, the clues are often in the words.

Think through a problem.

Let's take a simple problem and work it through. By using clues to decode this example, you can practice some steps that help you solve other problems that are not so simple. Don't rush to get an answer. Let's take the problem apart slowly so you can learn how to solve real problems later on. Here's the problem.

Example 1:
Counting envelopes
Step One

After mailing 13 letters, you have 15 empty envelopes left. How many empty envelopes did you start with?

Read the problem and figure out what question it asks. **What are you trying to find?** A question mark is an important clue. It identifies a question that's being asked. But you may have to reread the question to find *exactly* what the problem is asking for.

In this example, the question is "How many empty envelopes did you start with?" The words "How many empty envelopes" and "did you start with" are important clues. They tell you that you are trying to find out **how many envelopes you had before** you mailed some of them.

Step Two

Read the problem *again,* and this time, as you read, **picture the situation** in your mind.

Look for clues that tell you what is going on in the problem. Try to find words that help you see how the numbers are related. What are other clues in the problem? Do you see that the words—"left after" and "start"—also give you important clues about the problem?

Think about the clues and your mental picture until you understand what's happening in the problem. Ask yourself: *What is the situation or the story in this problem?*

Draw a rough sketch that represents what is going on in the problem. You don't have to be an artist! Figure 1 shows one possible sketch for the example.

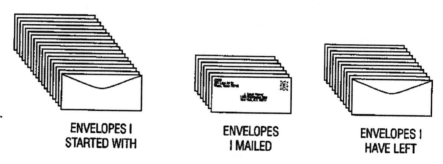

ENVELOPES I STARTED WITH

ENVELOPES I MAILED

ENVELOPES I HAVE LEFT

Figure 1
Draw a picture of the situation.

Step Three

Now is the time to put in the specific numbers for the problem. **Add the numbers to your rough sketch,** and add the symbols (such as +, −, ×, ÷, =) that you need to tell how the numbers relate to each other.

In the example, the numbers are 15 and 13. Figure 2 shows where those numbers belong in the sketch.

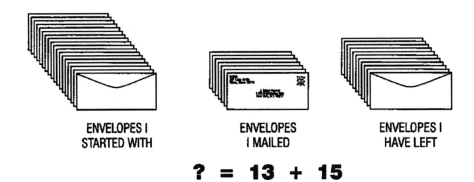

ENVELOPES I
STARTED WITH

ENVELOPES
I MAILED

ENVELOPES I
HAVE LEFT

? = 13 + 15

Figure 2
Add mathematics symbols to your picture.

Step Four

Now that you have a picture of the situation and have put in the mathematical symbols and numbers, you are ready to calculate. Before you calculate, review the question in Step One—*What are you trying to find?*

In the example, the question was this: *How many envelopes did you start with?* The picture in Figure 2 makes it clear that the answer to that question can be found by adding 15 and 13. **Do the calculations**—in your head, with a pencil, with your calculator, or a combination of all three!

Step Five

The last step is the most important. Make sure that you have not just *an* answer, but the *correct* one! *First,* put units on the number that you got in Step Four. 15 + 13 = 28. But 28 what? The answer is 28 envelopes. *Second,* read the problem (again!) for the last time and **check to see if your answer makes sense. Does it answer the question asked?**

One way to check your answer is to put it back into the problem and see if the problem then makes a true statement. Another way to check is to put your answer back into the picture that you drew and see if it makes sense. Do the numbers work out correctly?

In the example, the question asked how many envelopes you started with. If you started with 28 envelopes and you mailed 13 of them, would you have 15 envelopes left? Yes. Try putting 28 envelopes into the picture in Figure 2. Does the situation make sense and do the numbers work out? Yes. The correct answer is 28 envelopes.

CORD Workforce Mathematics 1

Advantages of thinking through a problem

Each time you work a problem, take time and think it through. Use a plan similar to the step-by-step plan we've outlined. If it is a type of problem you have thought through carefully before, you may recognize it right away. Then you can quickly make a sketch and write the numbers and symbols that express the situation.

Often on the job you see the same type of problem over and over again. Once you have **thought through that type of problem,** you can do it again, much more quickly and easily. You develop confidence in your calculations and in your answer.

Solving a sample problem

Example 2:
Counting connectors

Try this problem:
As you assemble printed circuit boards, you must attach one connector to each board. You have 9 connectors left after assembling 37 boards. How many connectors did you have before you assembled some boards?

Can you tell that this problem is exactly the same type as the envelope problem? Of course, the answer is *not* exactly the same, but you can find it exactly the same way.

Here are five steps again that help you think through this problem:

Step One

Read the problem. Figure out what question it asks. What are you trying to find?

Step Two

Draw a picture. Read the problem again and develop a picture of it in your mind. Look for clues to help you decode the problem. Draw a rough sketch that shows the situation.

Step Three

Put numbers in your rough sketch. Again, search for clues—words and numbers—that help you see how to do this.

Step Four

Do the calculations. Review the question *"What am I trying to find?"* Then do the calculations.

Check the result! Put the correct units on your answer. Then check to see if your answer makes sense in the problem. That is, does it answer the question asked?

Sketching a picture of the problem

Let's do the first two steps together. Then you can finish the three remaining steps. The first step is to read the problem carefully and decide what it's all about. Here's the problem restated:

> *You have 9 connectors left after assembling 37 boards. How many connectors did you have before you assembled some boards?*

What does the problem ask for? It asks you to find the **number of connectors** you had **before you used some of them.** You used 37 and you have 9 left. Therefore, you know that your answer, when you get it, ought to be **larger than** either 9 or 37. It's always helpful to have a rough idea of the size of your answer before you solve for it.

Now that you've read the problem carefully, figured out that it asks for "a certain number of connectors," and reasoned that your answer ought to be larger than 37, it's time to try Step 2—"Draw a Picture."

You don't have to know what a connector looks like to draw or sketch the problem. You don't need to draw connectors—just a heap that represents them. It is helpful to make the heap for 37 connectors bigger than the heap for 9 connectors. You can see the situation better if the sizes, as they relate to each other, are correct.

Figure 3 shows one way to draw a rough sketch for Example 2.

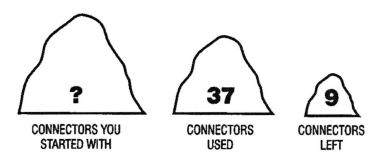

Figure 3
Make a rough sketch.

Study Activity: Work through the remaining three steps for this example problem. Did you put numbers on your drawing? Did you get 46 connectors for your answer? Did you check your answer to make sure it made sense? How would your picture change for the problem that follows?

How many connectors do you have left if you start with 100 and use 45 to assemble the circuit boards?

READING THE PROBLEM

Now let's look at some sample problems and practice each of the five steps. Let's start by just taking the first step with these problems.

Step One

Read the problem. Figure out what question it asks. What are you trying to find?

Study Activity: Here are ten sample problems to help you practice the first step in thinking through a problem. Do not find the answers (yet) to the following problems! Just write on your paper what you are **trying to find.** Include the units. For example, for the first problem, you might write *Find how many dollars Luis pays.* Do the same for Problems 2 through 10.

   1. Luis is going to pay for ⅓ of a boat. If the boat costs $5400, what is his share?

   2. Luis's sister will pay for the rest of the boat. What is her share?

3. Susan purchases two cordless drills for each of the six construction crews. How many cordless drills does she purchase?

4. Susan purchases 120 pounds of screws to share equally with the crews. How many pounds of screws should she give to each construction crew?

5. The warehouse has 7 cases of oil and receives a delivery of 23 more cases. How many cases of oil does the warehouse have after the delivery?

6. If the warehouse manager needs an inventory of 48 cases, how many more should be ordered?

7. An electrician uses 23½ feet of wire from a 50-foot roll. How much wire is left on the roll?

8. The electrician needs 8¼ feet of wire for each connection. How many connections will a 50-foot roll of wire supply?

9. Bob earns $380 a week and 20% of that is withheld for taxes and insurance. What amount is withheld each week?

10. In the situation in Problem 9, how much money does Bob take home each week?

The problems in the Study Activity above are arranged in pairs. The situation is the same for 1 and 2 but the question is different. Notice that 3 and 4 describe the same situation, and so on down the list.

These paired problems show how the same situation can lead to several different kinds of problems.

Whenever you work several problems together, on the job or in class, look to see if they are related. This helps you figure out the situation in each problem.

Check the answers to see if the information and data support your answers. Making judgments, guessing, and stating opinions are pitfalls to avoid in checking answers.

PICTURING THE PROBLEM

Step Two

Draw a picture. Read the problem again and picture it in your mind. Look for clues to help you decode the problem. Draw a rough sketch that shows the situation.

Let's talk about Step Two before you try it on the ten problems.

Sometimes there may be numbers in a problem that you will not use—extra clues. The words in a problem, as well as the numbers, provide clues that help you decode the situation and picture it correctly.

Words sometimes give clues that have more than one possible meaning. When you read the words "Hand me the file," what picture do those words form in your mind? *File* can mean, for instance, wood file, metal file, a rattail file, a diskette file, a fingernail file, or even a file folder to hold papers. Figure 4 shows some possible meanings for the word *file*. The word alone is not enough; you have to know more to determine what kind of file is meant.

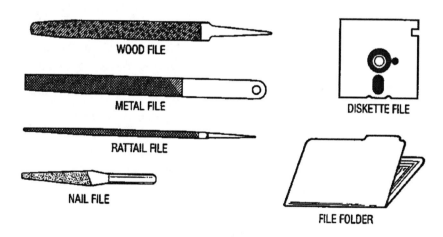

Figure 4
One word can have many meanings.

If you are standing in an office, *file* probably means a folder with papers inside or a collection of data records stored electronically on a computer disk. If you are in a woodshop, you would probably reach for a rasp of some kind. In a hair salon, you would know that *file* means a nail file. You can tell what a word means more accurately if you know the **context**—the situation in which the word is used.

As you read a mathematics problem, decide what **words** mean by reading them in the **context of the problem.** The same word can have different meanings in different contexts or situations.

Search for clues

As you read a problem carefully to understand it, there are clues that help tell you what is happening in the situation described in the problem. Numbers are clues, and a question mark or the word *find* can be a clue. What mathematics symbols (+, −, ×, ÷, =) should you use to represent the numbers and relationships between the numbers in the problem? Often certain words can be clues as you decide. The clues help remind you to think about certain possibilities.

What clues cannot do

Words, such as *total, how many, how much,* help you figure out what to do. However, no list of words can do your thinking for you! You must understand the problem before you can be sure what mathematics operation (+, −, ×, ÷) you need to do.

What does it mean to *understand* the problem?

You understand the problem when you have changed it in your mind from words on a page to a real situation with real people and things.

You understand the problem when you know exactly what information you have and what information you need to find.

After you *understand* the problem, you can decide what arithmetic operations will help you solve it. Clues help you consider what mathematics operations you might use in the context of the problem. You may need to use your calculator, or ask for more information, or get some help to work the problem. Understand the problem first and then do the math to solve it.

Now, in the activity below, do Step Two for the ten problems you worked before.

Study Activity: Again, don't find the answer to these problems! Read the problem again and picture it in your mind. Look for clues to help you decode it, and then draw a **rough** sketch or model that shows the situation.

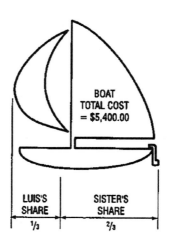

Figure 5
**Rough sketch showing how Luis and his sister
share the cost of a boat**

For example, Figure 5 shows how Luis and his sister share the cost of a boat. The same sketch can be used to represent the situation in both Problems 1 and 2. Note that you need to draw only a "cloud" or a "box" for the boat. But it helps if you draw the ⅓ and ⅔ shares more or less to scale.

1. Luis is going to pay for ⅓ of a boat. If the boat costs $5400, what is his share?

2. Luis's sister will pay for the rest of the boat. What is her share?

3. Susan purchases two cordless drills for each of the six construction crews. How many cordless drills does she purchase?

4. Susan purchases 120 pounds of screws to share equally with the crews. How many pounds of screws should she give to each construction crew?

5. The warehouse has 7 cases of oil and receives a delivery of 23 more cases. How many cases of oil does the warehouse have after the delivery?

6. If the warehouse manager needs an inventory of 48 cases, how many more should be ordered?

7. An electrician uses 23½ feet of wire from a 50-foot roll. How much wire is left on the roll?

8. The electrician needs 8¼ feet of wire for each connection. How many connections will a 50-foot roll of wire supply?

9. Bob earns $380 a week and 20% of that is withheld for taxes and insurance. What amount is withheld each week?

10. In the situation in Problem 9, how much money does Bob take home each week?

ADDING NUMBERS TO YOUR SKETCH

Step Three

Now is the time to put in the specific numbers for the problem. **Insert the numbers in your rough sketch,** and the symbols (such as +, −, ×, ÷, or =) you need to tell how the numbers relate to each other.

You probably already know most of the words that help you decide whether you should add, subtract, multiply, or divide to solve the problem. However, you may never have thought of these words as clues. Most people don't realize how important the words are. These little words can really help you decide how to work a problem. Let's examine some of these now.

Clues that may suggest addition

A problem that asks you to put together or combine different quantities is generally an addition problem. Figure 6 shows this.

The following list shows some words that often are used in mathematics problems as clues to addition. You may be able to think of words to add to this list. When you read these words in a problem, check the context, or situation, to see if these words are reminding you to think about addition:

total	sum	combined
how many	and	more
how far	together	additional
how much		

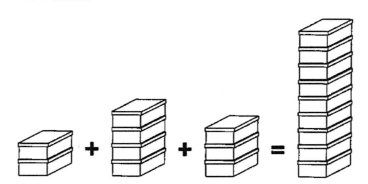

Figure 6
Addition combines various items.

Clues that may suggest subtraction

Notice that the combining words (how many, how much) that you saw in the addition clues may, in the context of the problem, be clues to subtraction also. The same words may occur in **both** addition and subtraction problems. So you always must read the problem carefully.

A problem that asks you to compare two quantities, that is, find how much more or how much less, is generally a subtraction problem. These words also signal a comparison of two quantities: remain, exceed, profit, change (money). Figure 7 pictures this and shows the symbol for subtraction.

Figure 7
Subtraction compares or reduces.

When you see these words in a mathematics problem, check the context to see if they are clues to subtraction:

remain	exceed	difference
profit	change (money)	diminished
how much more	how much is left	take away
reduced		

You often need to *add* some quantities and then *subtract* the total from another quantity. For instance, when you buy 3 items in a store, you first add the prices to find the total. Then you subtract the total from the money you hand the clerk to see what change you should receive.

Clues that may suggest multiplication

Have you ever thought you had enough money to buy an item and then discovered that you didn't because of the sales tax? Many states and towns add a sales tax to the total of your purchases. A tax is almost always a percentage (or part per 100 parts). To find the amount of a tax, you must multiply.

There is one word that, in a mathematics problem, usually means multiplication. When someone says "Give me half of that" the *of* is a clue to multiply by one-half. When you find 10% of 73, you multiply 73 by 0.10 to find the answer. When you find an area, you *multiply* one dimension by another.

The word *reduced* can be a clue to either subtraction or multiplication. If a weight is reduced by 5 pounds (a specific amount) *reduced* tells you to *subtract*. If the weight is reduced by 5% or ½₀ (a percent or fraction) reduced used with % tells you to *multiply* 5% (or ½₀) by the total to find the amount of the reduction (not the final weight).

To reduce by a specific amount—subtract. To reduce by a percent or fraction—multiply first to find the amount of the reduction and then subtract.

To see the difference, work through the following.

Study Activity:

1. The total number of names in the city telephone directory was reduced by 10,464 names this year. If there were 130,800 names last year, how many names are there this year?

2. The total number of names in the city directory was reduced by 8 percent this year. If there were 130,800 names last year, how many names were taken out this year?

3. How many names are *left* if last year's total of 130,800 was reduced by 8 percent?

Notice that you *subtract* the specific amount to answer Item 1. In Item 2, you *multiply* by the percent to find a specific amount. Then in Item 3 you subtract the specific amount to find out how many names are left.

The word "reduced" is a possible clue to subtraction but you sometimes may have to multiply first to find the specific amount to subtract.

Many problems require that you use more than one mathematics operation. The clues help you plan a solution, but you still must think about what the problem means. Your plan must include a sequence of the operations to solve the problem.

A problem that asks you to find a total for many items
of the same kind is probably a multiplication problem.
Area and volume problems often involve
multiplication.

Figure 8 shows how multiplication makes counting easier.

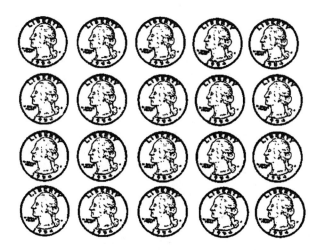

4 ROWS × 5 COINS PER ROW = 20 COINS
5 COLUMNS × 4 COINS PER COLUMN = 20 COINS

Figure 8
Multiplication combines the same items more
easily than does counting.

Here are some words and phrases that, in many problems,
may be clues to multiplication.

of	times	product
percent	each	cubic units
volume	per	how many
area	square units	reduced by a fraction
so many units at so much per unit		

Clues that may suggest division

If a problem asks you to separate something into equal parts
or shares, you probably will use division.

For example, suppose that an auto club of 10 members wants
to buy a used car to work on. The car costs $350. What is
each member's share of the cost? To divide the cost into

10 equal shares, one for each member, you would divide $350 by 10 ($350 ÷ 10) to get the answer of $35 per member.

You also use division to find an average for several numbers or quantities. You find an average by first adding all the numbers, or quantities, to get a total. After finding the total, you divide by the number of things you added to find the average. Write a plan to find the average of 16, 17, 19, and 20.

Study Activity:

Work the problem below with your calculator.

If the total cost of 24 cans of motor oil is $21.36, how much does each can cost?

Another way to ask the same question is "How much would one can cost?" or "What is the cost per can?"

A problem that asks you to divide a quantity into equal parts or shares, or to find the size of each part, is generally a division problem. Figure 9 shows a division into equal parts.

Here are some words and phrases that may remind you that numbers are to be divided.

each	average
equal parts	partition
shares	pieces
quotient	

12 ÷ 3 = 4

Figure 9
Division finds equal parts.

SETTING UP THE CALCULATIONS

In the *Introduction* to this chapter, you learned that there may be four or five ways to say the same thing. No wonder a math problem can be confusing at times! So far we've discussed three of the steps that can help you think your way through a problem and get the correct answer.

In the first step you read the problem very carefully and look for the clues. In the second step, you try to understand the problem by changing it in your head from words on the page to a real situation. For example, you imagine cans of motor oil, or rolls of electrical wire, or nails and then do a rough sketch on your paper. In the third step, you put numbers on the sketch and try to figure out which mathematics operation you should use to begin calculating.

Once you have decoded the clues and sketched the situation, you can tell what operation you need to perform—add, subtract, multiply, divide, or some combination of these.

Let's return to the ten problems we've been working on. Practice putting the correct mathematics symbols (+, −, ×, or ÷) in your sketch of each problem.

Study Activity:

On your own paper, *write the numbers and mathematics symbols* that tell which calculator keys you will need to press to work the problem. Just *decide* which operation you will do. Don't work the problem yet! For some problems, you may need to do more than one operation. Don't forget the equal sign (=) at the end of the operation. Figure 10 shows how this might look for Problems 1 and 2.

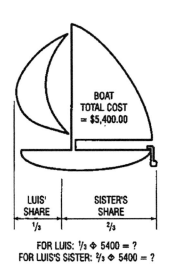

BOAT
TOTAL COST
= $5,400.00

LUIS' SHARE	SISTER'S SHARE
⅓	⅔

FOR LUIS: ⅓ ◊ 5400 = ?
FOR LUIS'S SISTER: ⅔ ◊ 5400 = ?

Figure 10
Getting the equation ready for calculation

1. Luis is going to pay for ⅓ of a boat. If the boat costs $5400, what is his share?

2. Luis's sister will pay for the rest of the boat. What is her share?

3. Susan purchases two cordless drills for each of the six construction crews. How many cordless drills does she purchase?

4. Susan purchases 120 pounds of screws to share equally with the crews. How many pounds of screws should she give to each construction crew?

5. The warehouse has 7 cases of oil and receives a delivery of 23 more cases. How many cases of oil does the warehouse have after the delivery?

6. If the warehouse manager needs an inventory of 48 cases, how many more should be ordered?

7. An electrician uses 23½ feet of wire from a 50-foot roll. How much wire is left on the roll?

8. The electrician needs 8¼ feet of wire for each connection. How many connections will a 50-foot roll of wire supply?

9. Bob earns $380 a week and 20% of that is withheld for taxes and insurance. What amount is withheld each week?

10. In the situation in Problem 9, how much money does Bob take home each week?

CARRYING OUT THE CALCULATIONS

With the equation set up, you are ready to use your calculator and solve for the answer.

Step Four

Do the calculations. Review the question "What am I trying to find?" before you start.

Study Activity:

Use the equations you wrote down for each of the ten problems and your calculator to find the answers to the problems. Write the answers on your paper.

1. Luis is going to pay for ⅓ of a boat. If the boat costs $5400, what is his share?

2. Luis's sister will pay for the rest of the boat. What is her share?

3. Susan purchases two cordless drills for each of the six construction crews. How many cordless drills does she purchase?

4. Susan purchases 120 pounds of screws to share equally with the crews. How many pounds of screws should she give to each construction crew?

5. The warehouse has 7 cases of oil and receives a delivery of 23 more cases. How many cases of oil does the warehouse have after the delivery?

6. If the warehouse manager needs an inventory of 48 cases, how many more should be ordered?

7. An electrician uses 23½ feet of wire from a 50-foot roll. How much wire is left on the roll?

8. The electrician needs 8¼ feet of wire for each connection. How many connections will a 50-foot roll of wire supply?

9. Bob earns $380 a week and 20% of that is withheld for taxes and insurance. What amount is withheld each week?

10. In the situation in Problem 9, how much money does Bob take home each week?

Finishing the problem

Step Five   **Check the result.** Put the correct units on your answer. Then check to see if your answer makes sense in the problem and if it answers the question asked.

Study Activity: Go back to each of your answers for the ten problems and write the correct units (dollars, screws, cases, and so forth). Your calculator cannot tell you the units!

Checking the answer

Then put each answer back into the problem. Check to see if you have answered the question asked in the problem. Does your answer make sense? Correct any mistakes you find.

USING THE MEMORY ON YOUR CALCULATOR

In this section, you practice working problems that may have more than one operation. Sometimes it is useful to use the *memory* on your calculator to work these problems.

Your calculator probably has a memory. The memory on a calculator is a storage place to keep a number you want to use later. Putting a number in memory is similar to jotting it down on a piece of scratch paper. Later, when you need it, you can bring the number out of memory. This is similar to looking at the number you wrote on the piece of scratch paper. All of this is summed up in Figure 11.

Figure 11
The calculator memory

Calculators are not all the same, so you will need to find out how the memory on your calculator works. The directions that came with your calculator may help you do this, or you can ask someone. The keys on your calculator may not be marked the same as the one we talk about here, but it probably has keys that do the same thing.

Usually there is a key labeled M+ that lets you add a number to the memory. Find the key on *your* calculator that adds a number into the memory. How is it marked? **Pressing the M+ key adds the number in the display window to the number in memory.** The number in the display window stays the same.

Many calculators also have a key labeled RM (for Recall Memory). **The RM key makes a copy of the number in memory and displays it in the window.** This erases the previous number in the display window but the number in memory stays the same.

On many calculators, when you put a number into the memory, a small M appears in the display window. This M reminds you that you have a number in memory.

When you press the CA (or Clear All) key, you clear the display window *and* the memory. Some calculators have a CM key to Clear the Memory. Always clear the memory before you start any problem. When the memory is empty, or has only zero in it, the M does not show in the display window.

Solving problems with the help of the memory key

At this time, you might work the following example problems faster with pencil and paper than with your calculator. However, use these problems to learn how the memory on your calculator works. *After* you have practiced using the memory, you might find that using your calculator is a real help as you work other problems.

Example 3:
Keeping up with an inventory

A company has batteries stored in five different warehouse locations. At the beginning of the month, the different warehouses report inventories of 123, 80, 45, 231, and 189 batteries. During the month, two outgoing shipments are made, one of 100 and one of 200 batteries. Also during the month, there are incoming shipments of 120, 48, and 72 batteries. What is the total inventory at the beginning and at the end of the month?

Use your calculator and follow these steps to work the problem.

1. Clear your calculator and the memory.

2. With your calculator, add the five beginning inventories to find the total for the beginning of the month. Key in 123 + 80 + 45 + 231 + 189 = and then write down this number as the answer to the first part of the question. Did you get 668 for the beginning total?

3. While you still have the beginning total in the display window, press the "memory" key to add this total to the calculator memory. The memory now has the beginning total in it. Notice the little M in the display window.

4. You now can key in a new number and the calculator will start a new problem. Add together the outgoing shipments by pressing the keys for 100 + 200 = so that the display window shows the total number of 300 batteries removed from inventory during the month.

Now you need to *subtract* this total of 300 from the beginning total that is in the memory.

    a. With some calculators you can do this by pressing a key labeled M– to subtract the number 300 in the display window from the number in memory (668).

    b. With other calculators you press the +/– key to change the number in the window to –300 and then press the M+ key to combine the –300 and the total that is stored in memory (668). This is the same as subtracting the 300 outgoing shipments from the beginning total of 668. The calculator works (668 – 300) as (–300 + 668).

5. Now the memory holds the beginning total minus the transfers. To add the incoming shipments, press the keys

120 + 48 + 72 =. The total of the incoming shipments is now in the display window. Does it show 240?

6. To add this incoming amount to the total in memory, press the M+ key. Now the memory holds the total inventory for the end of the month.

7. To see the contents of the memory, press the RM (or Recall Memory) key. The number you see in the display window is the answer to the second part of the question. Write this answer down, too.

8. If you did not get a beginning inventory of 668 batteries and an ending inventory of 608 batteries, start over again with Step 1 and follow the steps again slowly and carefully. If you still do not get these answers, ask for help. Your calculator may work in a different way.

Now use the memory on your calculator to work this problem.

Study Activity:

Pat begins the month with $178 in a checking account. During the month, she deposits (or puts into her account) checks for $13.76, $5.86, and $10.18. She writes checks for $23.67, $14.53, $9.08, and $4.20 that withdraw (or take out) money from her account. What is the total of her deposits? What is the total of her withdrawals? How much money does she have in her account at the end of the month?

Look at your answers to see if they are reasonable ones. If they are much too large or too small to fit the problem, carefully go through your calculations again.

The next example takes you through the steps to work a problem that uses the memory with multiplication.

Example 4:
Spending money on several items

You have $50 in cash in your wallet. You buy 6 items at $1.29 each, 17 items at $0.79 each, and 9 items at $2.56 each. How much money do you have left?

1. After you clear the calculator, key in 6 × $1.29 = to get the total for the first item.

2. Press the "memory" key to put this partial answer into the calculator memory. Clear the display window.

3. Now find the total for the second item.

4. Press the "add to memory" key to add this partial answer to the partial answer that is already in the memory. Clear the display window.

5. Find the total for the third item and add it to the memory.

6. Now the memory holds the total for all of the purchased items. To find the difference between this total and $50, enter $50 into the display window.

7. Press the – (subtraction) key and RM to recall the total from memory.

8. Press the = key.

The calculator works $50 – $44.21 in this way: –$44.21 + $50.

The display window shows how much money you have left. Do NOT turn the calculator off—this problem continues in the next example!

Example 5:
Calculating sales tax

When you get to the checkout counter, you remember that you have to pay sales tax. If the sales tax is 7¼%, do you have enough money to pay for your purchases and the tax?

1. The display window shows how much money you have left. What's in the memory? Press the RM key to see. The window now shows $44.21, the total of your purchases.

2. To find the amount of the sales tax, you need to find 7¼% of $44.21. Remember what the word "of" signals? The problem now is to multiply $44.21 (already in the display window) by 7¼% to find the amount of tax.

How do you put 7¼% into the calculator? Before you press any keys, do a little thinking. Read what follows to help you think this through.

Do you remember how to write 7¼% as a decimal? If not, you can simply work out 7¼ on the calculator: 7 + 1 ÷ 4. The answer will be 7.25. Does that look familiar? So, 7¼% is 7.25% or 7.25/100 or 0.0725. Now it will be easier to multiply by 7¼% with your calculator.

3. With $44.21 in the display window, press the × key and then key in 0.0725 and = to find the amount of the tax. Notice that your calculator is figuring this with more than two decimal places. Just keep the money in that form until you get to the very end of the problem.

4. You have to pay the tax plus the cost of your purchases. Press the "add to memory" key to add the number in the display window to the memory.

5. The memory now holds the total you will have to pay, including tax. Press the RM key to see this final total. Do you have enough money?

6. To find out exactly how much change you should get, key in $50, press the (−) key, then the RM key to recall the amount in memory, then the = key. Your calculator probably shows that you should get a little more than $2.58 in change. This calculator answer, rounded off to two decimal places, is $2.58. That's your change.

7. What really would happen is this. The clerk first would round the tax up to $3.21. Add that amount to your purchase total and then subtract that from $50 to see how the clerk would figure your change. Are the amounts the same?

You can use the memory in your calculator to do all kinds of problems—add, subtract, multiply, and divide.

Here is summary of what you have just practiced:

> The M+ (Add to Memory) key adds the number in the window display to whatever number is in the memory.

> The RM (Recall Memory) key copies the number in the memory to the display.

> The CM (Clear Memory) key clears just the memory.

> The CA (Clear All) key clears everything. On most calculators, this includes what's in memory.

> To subtract a number in memory from some quantity, key in the quantity, then the minus (−) sign, and then the RM key to recall the number in memory. The answer will appear in the display window after you press the = key.

SUMMARY

Treat a problem as a puzzle to be solved. Look for clues to help you decode the words and find the answer.

Use these five steps in your plan to solve problems:

Step One   **Read the problem.** Figure out what question it asks. What are you trying to find?

Step Two   **Picture the problem in your mind.** Look for clues to help you decode the problem. Then draw a rough sketch that shows the situation.

Step Three   **Add numbers to your rough sketch.** Again, search for clues—words and numbers—that help you see how to do this.

Step Four   Review the question *"What are you trying to find?"* Then **do the calculations.**

Step Five   Put the **correct units** on your answer. Then **check** to see if your answer makes sense in the problem and if it answers the question asked.

As you read a mathematics problem, decide what the words mean by reading them in the context of the problem. The same word can have different meanings in different contexts or situations. Look for clues that tell you what is going on in the problem. Try to find words that help you see how the numbers are related.

The most important advantage of taking the time to carefully think through a problem is this: Once you are sure you understand the problem and the situation, you develop confidence in your calculations and in your answer. Checking your answer by putting it back into the situation helps you catch errors.

Your calculator has keys for four basic mathematics operations—add, subtract, multiply, and divide.

A problem that asks you to put together or combine quantities is generally an addition problem.

A problem that asks you to compare two quantities (find how much more or how much less) is generally a subtraction problem.

A problem that asks you to find a total for many items of the same kind is generally a multiplication problem. Area and volume often involve multiplication.

A problem that asks you to separate a quantity into *equal* parts or shares, or to find the size of *each* part, is probably a division problem.

Use the memory of your calculator to help you work problems that have several steps and more than one operation:

The M+ (Add to Memory) key adds the displayed number to whatever number is in the memory.

The RM (Recall Memory) key copies the number in the memory to the display.

The CM (Clear Memory) key clears just the memory.

The CA (Clear All) key clears everything. On some calculators this includes what's in memory.

To subtract a number in memory from some quantity, key in the quantity, then the minus (–) sign, and then press the RM key to recall the number in memory. The answer will appear in the display window after you press the = key.

To figure out what you need to do, **read the problem very carefully and look for the clues.** Try to understand the problem by changing it in your head from words on a page to a real situation. Imagine cans of motor oil, or fence posts, or nails. Then do a rough sketch on your paper. Often you know which mathematics operations to carry out if you can imagine yourself in the real situation described by the written words.

PRACTICING THE SKILLS

Laboratory Activity

Use the mathematics skills you have learned to complete the following activity:

Activity   **Material estimates and costs**

Equipment   Measuring tape
Price list for:
     ¾-inch PVC pipe, 10-foot sections
     ¾-inch PVC unions
     ¾-inch 90° PVC elbows
Calculator

Statement of Problem   In the workplace, supervisors must often prepare written instructions. These instructions provide employees directions on how to complete a project. The success of a project depends on how carefully the instructions are written and how carefully employees read them.

In this activity, each group will prepare written instructions for a project assigned by your teacher. Once the instructions are completed, groups will exchange instructions and attempt to complete the project. Near the end of class, groups will come together and discuss ways of making the instructions clearer or easier to follow.

Situation: A temporary cold water line is needed in your classroom. This line should start at the nearest source of water and terminate at a location selected by your teacher. The material for this line is ¾-inch PVC pipe, which comes in standard 10-foot sections. One condition is that all pipe must run along the floor next to the wall. To meet this condition, your group may need to use both ¾-inch PVC unions (straight pipe to join sections) and ¾-inch 90° PVC elbows (curved pipe for the turns).

Procedure   **a.** Obtain the equipment listed above from your teacher.

b. Find from your teacher the nearest source of water and the termination point of the cold water line. Based on the situation above, have your group write instructions for laying the cold water line.

c. 1. Exchange instructions with another group and carry out the instructions your group receives. Do exactly what the instructions say, even if your group thinks they are wrong.

2. Determine how much pipe material is needed and the cost.

d. Discuss the results your group obtained by following the instructions written by the other group. Did your group do what the instructions said? Did your group do what the other group wanted them to do? Could the instructions have been clearer?

e. Based on these discussions, have your group rewrite the instructions to make them clearer and easier to follow. Ask your teacher to review your final set of instructions.

STUDENT EXERCISES

You can solve the exercises that follow by applying the mathematics skills you've learned. The problems described here are those you may meet in the world of work.

Note: *Wherever possible, use your calculator to solve the problems that require numerical answers.*

EXERCISE 1: A power company charges customers $0.1259 per kilowatt-hour for electricity. You are checking this month's bill. At the beginning of the month the meter reading was 7411 kilowatt-hours. At the end of the month the meter reading was 7996 kilowatt-hours.

a. How many kilowatt-hours of electricity did you use during the period?

b. How much should you be charged for the electricity used?

EXERCISE 2: A local package-delivery service limits the package weight to 30 pounds. You fill a box with thermostats. Each thermostat weighs ¾ lb. You weigh the box before sealing it and find that it weighs 35½ lb.

a. How many thermostats should you remove to meet the 30-pound limit?

b. You want to ship 38 thermostats in one package. What is the maximum total weight that the box and packing material can be?

EXERCISE 3: Robert and Misty bought a new house. They are figuring out how much sod they need to cover their front yard. The front yard is rectangular. One side measures 20 yards. The other side measures 12 yards. See diagram below.

a. What is the area of Robert and Misty's front yard?

(Hint: Area is calculated by multiplying the length × width.)

b. How many "yards" (that is, square yards) of sod will it take to cover the front yard?

c. Robert and Misty decide to spread out the sod so that they need only ¾ of the full amount. How many "yards" of sod should they buy?

EXERCISE 4: What is the total cost for the purchase of 25 ½" heavy-duty straight-shank bits selling for $12.50 each, and 4 dozen ⅜" corner router bits selling for $6.25 each?

EXERCISE 5: A manufacturer made the following purchases of electrodes for arc welders.

February 10	25 cartons at $19.35 each
April 7	60 cartons at $19.50 each
June 21	50 cartons at $20.05 each
August 25	40 cartons at $19.50 each

a. What is the total number of cartons purchased?

b. What was the total cost of the purchases for each of the four months?

c. What was the total cost of all purchases?

d. On October 1, the manufacturer has 22 cartons of electrodes left in inventory. How many cartons of electrodes has the manufacturer used?

EXERCISE 6: Suppose you start out with a savings account balance of $358.68. Then you make deposits of $87.15, $126.43, and $125.00. The final deposit slip indicates a balance of $711.21.

a. What is the total of your deposits?

b. What is the sum of the initial balance and the three deposits?

c. The difference between the sum computed above in Part b and the balance shown on the deposit slip is the interest the bank has credited to your account. How much is that?

EXERCISE 7: You are the warehouse manager for the Lunar Candy Bar Factory. You have on hand a total inventory of 461,200 candy bars in three warehouse buildings. The company president instructs you to reduce the warehouse space to two buildings. Each warehouse building has a maximum capacity of 200,000 bars. You know that it's best to keep on hand 90% of the maximum warehouse capacity.

a. How many candy bars will you want to keep on hand in each warehouse building?

b. At this level, what would be the total inventory in the two warehouse buildings?

c. How many candy bars must be sold to reduce the current inventory to the number you want to keep on hand in the two buildings?

EXERCISE 8: Leases, Inc. offers 48-month automobile leases on the Royale line of cars for $322 per month with a mileage allowance of 60,000 miles. The agency charges 6¢ per mile for travel over 60,000 miles. Suppose you leased a Royale for 48 months and drove it a total of 72,910 miles.

a. What is the total of the monthly lease payments you must make for the 48-month agreement?

b. By how much did you exceed the 60,000 mileage allowance?

c. How much will you have to pay for excess mileage?

d. What is the total of your payments to Leases, Inc. for the Royale?

EXERCISE 9: An advertisement for an air-conditioning unit indicates that this unit will use $263 in electricity per year.

a. At this rate, if you used the unit for six warm-weather months, how much would the electricity cost you during each of these summer months?

b. If a competing brand advertises that it uses ⅒ less energy, how much would the electricity cost to run this unit?

EXERCISE 10: For the first 10 days in a hospital, an insurance policy pays $105 per day for hospital care. A patient is discharged from the hospital after an eight-day stay with a total bill of $1238.00.

a. What amount will the insurance company pay?

b. The patient is responsible for the portion of the bill not paid by the insurance company. How much must the patient pay?

EXERCISE 11: A metal part is to be machined to a width of 1.285 inches. The stock width is 2.000 inches. How much of the stock must be removed?

EXERCISE 12: You work for G & W's Garage. The end gap of the piston rings in the automobile you are working on should be 0.020". Using a feeler gauge, you measure the distance (gap) between the ends of a new piston ring. The gap measures 0.017". How much of the ring end material must be removed with a file to obtain the correct end gap?

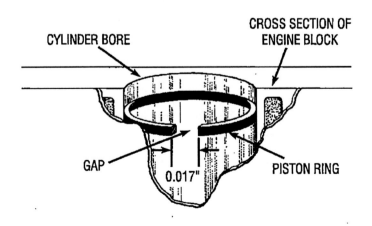

CYLINDER BORE

CROSS SECTION OF ENGINE BLOCK

GAP

0.017"

PISTON RING

EXERCISE 13:   A neon electric sign uses 4½ watts of electrical power per hour for each foot of tubing. How many watts will be used by a sign that is made of 26 feet of tubing?

EXERCISE 14:   The storeroom has 14 spools of wire in stock. Each spool contains 150 feet of wire.

a. What is the total length of wire on the spools?

b. A closer inspection reveals that one spool is tagged, indicating that 65 feet of wire have been removed from it. From this information, what is the total length of wire in the storeroom?

EXERCISE 15:   An order for structural steel calls for the following: 125 feet of channel iron weighing 3½ tons, 140 feet of I-beam weighing 4³⁄₁₀ tons, and 80 feet of angle iron weighing 2⅕ tons. The load limit of the delivery truck is 9½ tons. All of the channel iron and I-beam is loaded. But loading of the angle iron is stopped when the load limit of the truck is reached.

a. What is the total weight of structural steel ordered?

b. How many tons of angle iron will not be loaded?

EXERCISE 16:   Air-conditioning systems are charged with refrigerant R-134a. A full canister of R-134a contains 50 pounds of refrigerant. Each system that is charged uses 1¾ pounds of refrigerant. How many systems can be completely charged with refrigerant?

EXERCISE 17:   A common method for counting small parts is to weigh them. A finishing nail is a typical example. About 196 size-8d finishing nails make a pound.

a. What is the weight of each 8d nail?

b. If you buy five pounds of 8d finishing nails, about how many nails have you bought?

EXERCISE 18: Eight individually powered machines are used in a small production shop. Machine A uses 420 watts, machine B uses 255 watts, machine C uses 550 watts, machine D uses 480 watts, machine E uses 310 watts, machine F uses 515 watts, machine G uses 730 watts, and machine H uses 470 watts.

a. What is the total wattage used when all the machines are running at the same time?

b. The total wattage used must be limited to 3000 watts. Machines C, F, and G must be kept running. What is the fewest number of the other machines that can be turned off to keep the total power usage below 3000 watts?

EXERCISE 19: On a vacation trip, you plan to travel at an average speed of 60 miles per hour. The total distance you will travel is 1170 miles.

a. How many hours of driving will be needed to travel the total distance?

b. You expect one overnight stay of ten hours, two meal stops of ¾ hour each, and three fuel stops of ¼ hour each. What is the total time needed for your vacation trip?

EXERCISE 20: A film is used on automobile windows to reflect light. One manufacturer claims that its film allows only 35% of the light shining on a window to pass through and enter the car.

a. If 1240 watts from the sun shine on a window covered with this film, how much of the light passes through?

b. If this light passes through the first film, then passes through a second identical layer of film, what is the final amount of light that passes through the window? (Be careful.)

Chapter 4

Learning Problem-Solving Techniques

**How to apply a simple model of organized strategies
to solve problems**

Prerequisites

This chapter builds on mathematics skills you learned while taking mathematics courses up to the ninth-grade level. To complete this chapter, you should have a scientific calculator and know how to use it.

This chapter assumes you are familiar with numbers, fractions, decimals, percents, simple arithmetic operations, and calculator use.

To Master This Chapter

Read the text and answer all the questions. Complete the assigned exercises and activity. Work the problems on the chapter test at a satisfactory level.

Chapter Objectives

Working through this chapter helps you learn how to:

1. Read a problem and decide what is given and what is to be found.

2. Develop a plan for solving the problem.

3. Carry out your plan to solve the problem.

4. Check the answer and decide if it is reasonable.

LEARNING THE SKILLS

INTRODUCTION

You solve problems every day, but have you ever taken time to look at *how* you solve problems? If you understand the way you solve problems, you can handle problems you meet more easily, even hard ones. This chapter helps you explore the art of problem solving.

What is a problem?

You meet a problem when

- you need to know something you don't know.
- you must decide between different choices.
- you don't know what to do.

Mathematics helps you solve problems. Many times you need to know facts such as how much, how many, how often, how big, and how small before you can solve a problem.

You solve a problem when

- you find the information you need.
- you pick the best choice and carry it out.
- you figure out what to do and then do it.

Who solves problems?

Everyone does. On a job you spend lots of time solving problems. An auto mechanic figures out why a car engine is not working. A carpenter calculates how much lumber is needed for a job. A machinist determines the best sequence of operations to produce a part. Bank tellers are often challenged with finding errors in customers' accounts. The better you are at problem solving, the more successful you will be at your job.

THE GENERAL PLAN FOR PROBLEM SOLVING

There are many approaches to problem solving. You can simply guess, or guess and try to prove your guess is true, or make a table. Or you can tell a story, construct a chart or graph, make inferences, or draw conclusions from data. And there are still others.

You will become better at problem solving if your plan is organized and directed by strategies like the following:

- Using estimation to help you start
- Finding a trend or pattern
- Finding similar problems that have been solved
- Looking at the cause and the effect
- Reducing conditions when possible
- Constructing a table, graph, or formula
- Working backward
- Looking for key words, phrases, and other signals

A step-by-step plan that uses several of these strategies will help you learn and practice better problem-solving skills.

Whenever you meet a problem, carry out these four steps:

1. Understand the problem.
2. Develop a plan.
3. Carry out the plan.
4. Check the results.

Let's apply these four steps to the following problem:

Example 1:
Ordering supplies

Jean has just been hired as the office manager for XYZ Company. One of her first tasks is to order enough paper to take care of next month's needs. How much should she order?

Before you read how Jean solved her problem, get some paper and a pencil. Whenever you notice something that Jean overlooked, write it down.

1. First, Jean tries to *understand the problem*. She sees right away that she does not have enough information to solve the problem.

She studies the office layout and asks questions. She learns that she needs to order paper for all work stations: two typewriters, one copier, and four word processing stations. All stations need the same kind of paper.

Figure 1
Ordering office supplies

She learns from an office supply catalog that she must order the paper by the case. Each case contains 10 reams of paper.

2. Second, Jean *develops a plan*. She decides that she will check how much paper each of the three stations used during the last month and order that same amount for next month.

3. Next, Jean *carries out her plan*. She finds that 2 reams were used by the typists, 57 reams were used at the copier, and 18 reams were used by the word processing stations.

She calculates how much paper was used all together:

$$2 \text{ reams} + 57 \text{ reams} + 18 \text{ reams} = 77 \text{ reams}$$

Because she must order by the case, she divides 77 reams by 10 reams/case to determine how many cases she needs:

$$77 \text{ reams} \div 10 \text{ reams/case} = 7.7 \text{ cases}$$

However, she cannot order part of a case. She rounds her answer up to the nearest whole case and decides to order 8 cases.

4. Last, Jean asks herself, "Does this answer make sense?" She *rechecks her plan and her figures.* Everything seems in order. In addition, she checks the file for last month's order. She finds that the previous office manager ordered 7 cases last month. Jean believes that her decision to order 8 cases is reasonable. She places the order.

Jean developed an adequate plan to handle the situation, and her solution is reasonable. Can you think of any facts she might have overlooked? Can you come up with a different plan?

PRACTICING THE STEPS

Next, let's look at each separate part of the problem-solving process.

Understand the problem.

Example 2:
Fencing a storage area

A manufacturer wants to fence an outside storage area. Its four sides measure 1200 feet, 950 feet, 730 feet, and 850 feet. The wire chosen comes in 50-foot rolls.

How many rolls should he buy?

Here, *thinking* is the key. To understand the problem, first *check the facts* and then *organize the facts* so that you can decide which you need to use. Read over the problem until you form a mental picture of the situation. You can organize the facts by sketching on your paper the picture you formed in your mind or by rewriting the problem in your own words. These are summarized in Figure 2. Can you think of other ways that will help you understand the problem?

Check the facts.   *What do you know now?* Notice the facts given to you. Are they enough to solve the problem? Do you need more information? Do you need to use all of the given information? Can you figure out other facts from the ones you have?

What do you need to find? Make sure you know what question you are trying to answer. Otherwise, you might spend lots of time solving the wrong problem.

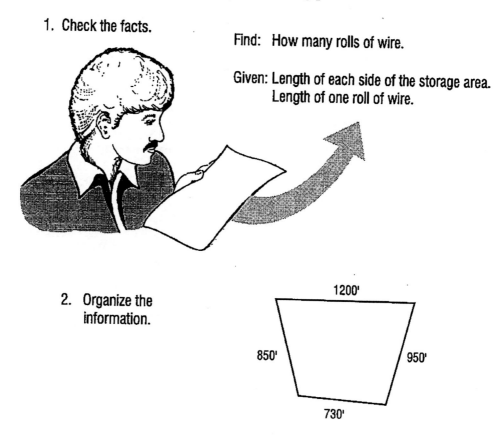

1. Check the facts.

Find: How many rolls of wire.

Given: Length of each side of the storage area.
Length of one roll of wire.

2. Organize the information.

1200'

850'   950'

730'

Figure 2
Understanding the problem

Organize the information.

Arrange the information so you can work with it. Try one of these methods:

- Draw a picture
- Make a list
- Make a chart
- Rewrite the problem in your own words

At this point, you still may not completely understand the problem. That's okay! Move on to the next step and try to develop a plan. Working on the plan will help you see what else you need to understand.

Develop a plan.

Thinking is the key here, too. Decide what action will lead to a solution. Look at Figure 3. Do the questions shown there make sense? Do the three steps outlined there help you develop a plan? You may see one or more ways to solve the problem right away. If so, choose the way that seems best to you, and move on to the next step.

Figure 3
Developing a plan

If you are puzzled, ask yourself these questions:

Is the problem familiar?

Have you seen a problem like this one before? Can you solve it the same way you've solved another problem? Can you get a hint from another problem?

What steps lead to an answer?

There are no rules that tell you *how* to make a plan. Use your reason and your experience. Keep your mind open and curious. Ask yourself, "What if...?" Try different approaches until you discover one that might work.

CORD Workforce Mathematics 1

Some of the different approaches you may find useful include:

- Draw a diagram
- Make a model
- Find a pattern
- Solve a simpler problem of the same type
- Use a known formula
- Use an equation
- Guess and check

The more problems you solve, the easier problem solving becomes. Solve enough in any one area and you become an expert!

What calculations are needed?

You may need to find out how *much*, how *many*, how *often*, or other facts to solve the problem. Apply your math skills and plan to use your calculator to help you.

Carry out the plan.

After you decide on a plan, shift from thinking to *action* and carry out your plan. Be ready to change your plan if you have a better idea or discover an error in your plan. Figure 4 shows how the manufacturer carried out the plan to determine how much fence wire was needed.

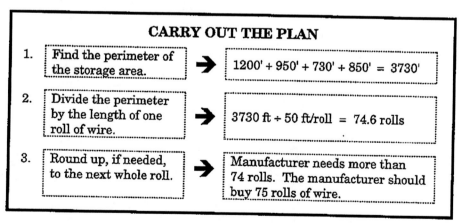

Figure 4
Carrying out the plan

Carrying out the plan is an **action** step. It's different from the first two. For example, when you decide to paint a room, you first think about the color and kind of paint to get. Then you develop a plan to measure the wall area to be painted and figure out how much paint to buy.

"Understanding the problem" and "developing a plan" are *thinking* steps. "Carrying out the plan" involves action. You use a measuring instrument to determine the size of the room. You use a calculator to figure the area of the walls and to calculate how much paint is needed.

In math problems, this step usually (but not always) involves calculations. That's why you've learned how to add, subtract, multiply, and divide numbers—including whole numbers, fractions, and decimals.

Check the results.

Last, *think* about your answer. Make sure it works for your problem. Ask yourself these questions:

Did I carry out the plan correctly?

Did I make any mistakes in my calculation? Do the numbers and the units make sense? Can I make an estimate of the calculations? Is the calculated answer close to my estimate?

Figure 5
Checking the results

CORD Workforce Mathematics 1

Did the plan work?

Is the answer reasonable for the problem? Does it answer the question?

Estimation is an important skill. It is useful in checking your results. This skill will be developed in Chapter 5, "Estimating Answers." You can use it now, but you will get better at it after covering Chapter 5.

PROBLEM-SOLVING EXAMPLES

For each example that follows, use these four problem-solving steps to find the solution to the problem:

1. Understand the problem.

2. Develop a plan.

3. Carry out the plan.

4. Check the results.

First, read the problem. Then write down on paper your plan to solve the problem. Carry out your plan and find an answer. After you finish, study the solution in the book. Your plan may be different from the example, but the answer should be the same.

Example 3:
Planning a weight-loss diet

Andy's company is promoting a physical fitness program. Andy needs to lose 20 pounds. He now eats about 2600 calories a day and his weight is not changing. His diet allows him 1600 calories a day. He knows that 3500 calories equal about 1 pound of fat. Andy wants to know how long it will take him to lose the 20 pounds. How many days will it take Andy to lose this weight?

Given   a. Andy now eats 2600 calories per day.
           b. Andy will eat 1600 calories per day.
           c. 3500 calories equal 1 pound of fat.
           d. Andy needs to lose 20 pounds.

Figure 6
Planning a diet for Andy

Find   How many days will it take Andy to lose 20 pounds?

Solution   Andy's plan:

1. Calculate how many calories he must give up to lose 20 pounds.

2. Calculate how many calories he must give up each day.

3. Divide the total calories he must give up by how many he gives up each day.

Andy's calculations:

1. 3500 cal/lb × 20 lb = 70,000 cal
   Andy needs to give up 70,000 calories in all.

2. 2600 cal − 1600 cal = 1000 cal
   Andy must give up 1000 calories each day.

3. 70,000 cal ÷ 1000 cal/day = 70 days
   It will take Andy 70 days to lose 20 pounds.

Check: Andy double-checks his calculations. Giving up 1000 calories a day for 70 days means he will give

up 70,000 calories in all, the amount needed to lose 20 pounds. The answer is reasonable.

Andy plans for the diet to take about 70 days.

Andy asks, "How many months is that?" If Andy assumes that a month is 30 days, what answer should he get?

Example 4:
Building a patio

Janet has a contract to build a backyard patio. The patio will measure 24 feet long by 18 feet wide. Janet will use concrete patio stones that measure 12 inches by 18 inches. The local hardware store sells the patio stones she needs for $0.45 each. How many patio stones should she buy? What will they cost?

Figure 7
Building a patio

Given

   a. Patio will measure 24' × 18'

   b. Each stone measures 12" × 18"

   c. Each stone costs $0.45

Find

   a. How many stones to buy

   b. Cost of the stones

Solution   To help her organize the information, Janet draws this picture:

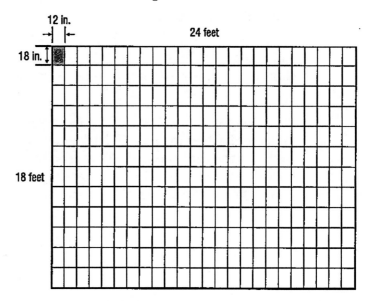

Janet decides to place the stones so that the 12-inch sides line up along the 24-foot length, and the 18 inches sides line up along the 18-foot width.

Janet's plan:

1. Calculate how many stones are needed to cover one patio length of 24 feet.

2. Calculate how many stones are needed to cover one patio width of 18 feet.

3. Multiply the number of stones for the patio length by the number of stones for the patio width.

4. Multiply the number of stones for the entire job by $0.45/stone.

Janet's calculations:

1. Janet needs to find how many 12-inch lengths there are in 24 feet. She changes 12 inches to 1 foot because she knows each number must be expressed in the same unit of measure. This calculation is now easy.

$$24 \text{ feet} \div 1 \text{ ft/stone} = 24 \text{ stones}$$

She needs 24 stones to cover the patio length.

2. Janet needs to find how many 18-inch lengths are in 18 ft. Again, she changes inches to feet.

Eighteen inches is 1.5 feet.

18 ft ÷ 1.5 ft/stone = 12 stones

She needs 12 stones for the patio width.

3. So, the total number of patio stones is

24 stones × 12 stones = 288 stones

She needs 288 stones in all.

4. The cost of the stones is:

288 stones × $0.45/stone = $129.60

The stones will cost Janet $129.60.

Check: Janet repeats her calculations to double-check her answers. The numbers appear correct. She compares the number of stones she calculated in Steps one, two, and three with her sketch. The numbers appear reasonable.

To do a rough estimate of the cost, she rounds off her numbers and thinks, "288 stones is almost 300 stones. The cost of $0.45/stone is almost the same as $0.50/stone. Three hundred stones at $0.50 each would cost $150. I rounded up each number, so my answer should be less than $150, and it is! So my answer is reasonable."

Based on her calculations, Janet decides to buy 288 stones for a cost of $129.60.

Example 5:
Semiconductor production

A semiconductor plant produces 10,000 silicon wafers per month. The company changes one element in the manufacturing process and increases its monthly output by 25%. The company estimates each wafer will produce 314 digital signal processor chips. How much does the monthly output total increase? How many more chips can the plant produce per month?

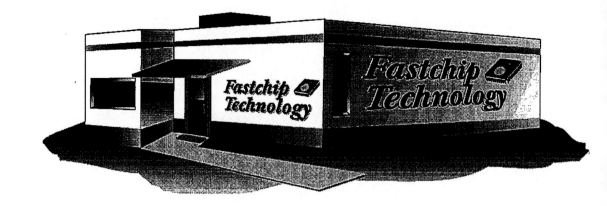

Figure 8
Semiconductor plant

Given a. 10,000 silicon wafers were produced each month before the streamlined manufacturing process was introduced.

b. A 25% increase in the monthly output is achieved as a result of the manufacturing process change.

c. 314 chips can be produced from each wafer.

Find a. How much does the monthly output total increase as a result of the new streamlined manufacturing process?

b. How much does the streamlined manufacturing process increase the number of chips produced each month?

Your plan:

1. Calculate 25% of 10,000 to determine the monthly output increase in the number of wafers.

2. Multiply the monthly output increase in the number of wafers by 314 chips per wafer to determine the increase in the number of chips produced each month.

Your calculations:

1. 10,000 wafers × 25% = 2,500 wafers

2. 2,500 wafers × 314 chips per wafer = 785,000 chips

Check: ¼ is the fraction equivalent of 25%, and ¼ of 10,000 is 2,500. Therefore, the answer of an increase of 2,500 wafers per month is reasonable. Round 314 chips to 300 chips and multiply by 2,500. The product is 750,000. Therefore, the answer of an increase of 785,000 chips produced per month is a reasonable answer.

SUMMARY

You solve problems every day. Much of your time is spent solving problems related to your work. If you understand the problem-solving process, you can handle problems more easily, even difficult ones.

Whenever you have a problem to solve, carry out these four steps:

1. Understand the problem.
2. Develop a plan.
3. Carry out the plan.
4. Check the results.

Thinking is the key to problem solving. You think as you understand the problem and develop a plan. Then you shift to *action* to carry out your plan.

Figure 9
Using the four problem-solving steps

PRACTICING THE SKILLS

Laboratory Activity

Use the mathematics skills you have learned to complete the following activity.

Activity: **Designing a cardboard container**

Equipment   Vernier caliper
Ruler
12-ounce soft drink can
Calculator

Given   You work in the drafting department of a packaging company. A preliminary design is needed for a cardboard container to hold six 12-ounce cans of soft drink for a bottling company. They have sent you a sample of the can and the following specifications for the container.

1. The package is to completely cover the six cans. They are to be arranged in two rows of three cans each. The two cans at each end will be exposed, as shown in the illustration.

2. The package will be glued together with a lengthwise overlap of ½ the outside diameter (OD) of a soft drink can.

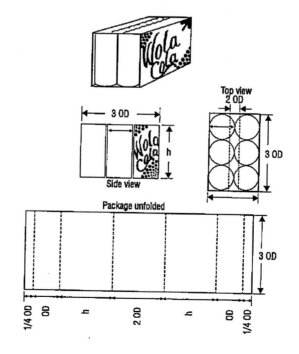

Find   The size of the cardboard (length and width) needed to make the package.

Procedure   *Understand the problem.*

1. What data do you have now to solve the problem?

2. What are you trying to find?

Develop a plan.

1. What additional information do you need to solve this problem?

2. Does finding any of this information involve solving other problems?

3. Are there any graphical methods you can use?

4. What computational methods can you use?

5. Is equipment available that you can use to find the needed information?

Note: Decide what additional information you need. Ask your teacher for this specific information. Your teacher will show you where to get the information or give you a source for it. Discuss your plan with your teacher.

Carry out the plan.

1. Solve the problem showing all of your work.

2. Can you make a rough estimate for any or all parts of the solution?

Check the results.

1. If you made rough estimates, compare the estimates to your calculated results.

2. For any part of the solution for which you did not make an estimate, calculate the result again to make sure there are no errors.

Activity Extension (Optional)

Given   The bottling company also would like to produce 16-ounce cans of the same soft drink and package them in the same way as the 12-ounce cans. The height of the 16-ounce can must remain the same as the 12-ounce can. So, only the outside diameter (OD) of the can will change.

Find   What size cardboard is needed to package six of the 16-ounce cans?

STUDENT EXERCISES

You can solve the exercises that follow by applying the mathematics skills you've learned. The problems described here are those you may meet in the world of work.

Note: Wherever possible, use your calculator to solve the problems that require numerical answers.

In this chapter, problem solving is the skill you are learning. For each of the assigned exercises, you should

- *Understand the problem.*
- *Develop a plan.*
- *Carry out the plan.*
- *Check the results.*

Your work should show <u>all four steps</u>.

EXERCISE 1:   Barney needs to repair or replace his 16-ft utility trailer. He has $1000 that he can spend. If he buys a new trailer, the dealer will allow him $1500 trade-in for his trailer. The new trailer costs $3200. The repairs that are needed include:

      New flooring $127

      Repair of frame and hitch $425

      Replace two tires $280

Barney has asked for your help. Develop a plan to tell him whether he should repair or replace his trailer.

a. What is his total cost to replace the trailer?

b. What is his total cost for repairing his old trailer?

c. What should he do?

EXERCISE 2:   You have a contract with Bess Truman High School to replace the tile in a 20-ft × 40-ft classroom. The school has 14 boxes of tile. The tile that is being used costs $33.75 per box. Each box covers 45 square feet.

a. Allowing for a total waste of 10%, how much additional tile is needed?

b. How much will it cost?

EXERCISE 3: A freight company is analyzing the eight-hour work rate of its four loading-dock crews. The dock supervisor reports to you that it takes about ½ hour for a crew to load each truck. Each employee takes breaks totaling one hour during each shift. Organize the information the company knows and determine how many trucks can be loaded during each eight-hour shift.

EXERCISE 4: You are the owner of a small construction company. As a sole proprietorship, your company is taxed at a rate of 60% on its gross profit of $200,000. You want to consider reorganizing your company as a Subchapter S corporation. The company under the new organization plan is taxed according to the following schedule.

First $25,000	17%
Second $25,000	20%
Third $25,000	30%
Fourth $25,000	40%
Remaining funds	46%

How much can your company save in taxes by reorganizing?

EXERCISE 5: You are a bookkeeper for Mountain Instruments. They are considering building a small plant in Westover, a town with a population of about 40,000. The total start-up cost for the plant is $350,000. The monthly expenses would be $5000 for utilities, $48,000 for payroll, and $300 for property taxes. The plant has a production capacity of 400,000 pieces per year. Each piece has a market value of $3.00. What gross profit or loss can the company expect the first year?

EXERCISE 6: You are the warehouse supervisor for a manufacturing company. Business is good and your crew is earning a lot of overtime pay. You need to decide if you should hire another order puller. You now have three order pullers. They get time-and-a-half for all time over 40 hours in a week. The total hours worked by each order puller for the last four weeks are given in the following table. All the order pullers are paid the same hourly wage. Should you hire another order puller?

	Week 1	Week 2	Week 3	Week 4
Albert	48 hr	50 hr	45 hr	52 hr
Mary	50 hr	49 hr	51 hr	45 hr
Bob	51 hr	48 hr	53 hr	50 hr

EXERCISE 7:   You are an assistant manager for a catalog order store. You have been asked for a recommendation about a minicomputer and software package to be used for customer-order tracking. The current method costs $23,500 per year. The computer system has an initial cost of $70,000. Not counting the initial cost, the computerized system expenses will be 11% less than the current method. How long will it take the system to pay for itself?

EXERCISE 8:   You are a buyer for a furniture manufacturer. The company is introducing a new line of bookshelves. You have decided to offer two models of shelves, one in oak and the other in pine. The shelves require 48 board feet of lumber. The labor cost is $8.00 per hour. The labor time required for the pine is 3.6 hours. The oak requires about 10% more labor time because it is a hardwood. The material cost is $0.70 per board foot for pine and $1.10 per board foot for oak. If the initial run is 70 shelves in pine and 40 in oak, what is the production cost for these shelves?

EXERCISE 9:   Your take home pay is $1500 each month. Your estimated expenses for November are given in the following table.

Estimated expenses for November

Car payment	$225
Church donation	$100
Entertainment	$35
Gas for car	$95
Groceries	$120
Meals out	$75

Rent	$350
Savings	$100
Telephone	$30
Utility bills	$185

Do you have enough money to pay your estimated expenses?

EXERCISE 10: You are a supervisor for Martex, a garment manufacturer. The sewing machines are old and often break down. The operators can produce an average of 50 units per hour when the machines are operating. The company makes a profit of $0.50 on each unit. The owner wants to know how much money is being lost because of down-time. You collect the following data on the four machines for a 40-hour period.

Machine 1	4.0 hr down
Machine 2	2.5 hr down
Machine 3	3.2 hr down
Machine 4	2.3 hr down

How much did the downtime cost the company?

EXERCISE 11: You are a sales representative for Biggs Motor Service. You have a customer who wants to know how many kilowatt-hours a 6-horsepower motor will use when operated 15 hours a day. You can determine the wattage by multiplying the horsepower rating by 1000. The number of watt-hours is found by multiplying the time in hours by the wattage. The number of kilowatt-hours is the watt-hours divided by 1000. What is the daily kilowatt-hour usage of the motor?

EXERCISE 12: Tracy is a programmer at Conroy Engineering. She has written a program to convert inches to centimeters. She tried her program with a series of data and got the following table. She asks you to check the results of the program. Is Tracy's program correct?

**Computer program-generated conversions
from inches to centimeters**

Inches	Centimeters
0	0.0
1	2.7
2	5.4
5	13.5
10	27.0

Use the formula,

$$\text{Centimeters} = \text{Inches} \times 2.54 \text{ centimeters per inch}$$

EXERCISE 13: You are a computer operator at Electronic Systems. The specifications for the equipment call for the room to be kept at a temperature of less than 20°C. The thermometer in the room is calibrated in Fahrenheit degrees instead of Celsius degrees. The temperature is 74°F. Should you call building maintenance to check on the air conditioning in your room? Convert the temperature from Fahrenheit to Celsius using the formula

$$\text{Temperature °C} = (\text{Temperature °F} - 32) \times \frac{5}{9}$$

EXERCISE 14: A machine at a bottling company is set to fill a two-liter bottle in 0.5 second and move the next bottle into place in 0.1 second. How many 2-liter bottles will the machine fill in one hour?

EXERCISE 15: A laser technician in the development division of a laser manufacturer is working on a laser that will deliver 50 watts. The beam normally has an area of 1.5 square centimeters, but can be focused down to a spot of 0.0001 square centimeter. The formula

$$\text{Power Density} = \frac{\text{Watts}}{\text{Area}}$$

is used to calculate the power density of the normal and focused beam. At power densities greater than 400,000 watts per square centimeter, damage to optics becomes a problem. Could this be a problem for the technician?

EXERCISE 16:   You are constructing a column assembly in a building. A ½"-thick plate secures the top and bottom of the column. The bottom plate rests on an 8" footing. A girder with a thickness of 8½" rests on the top plate. The total height must be 95¾", as shown below. To what length must the column be trimmed?

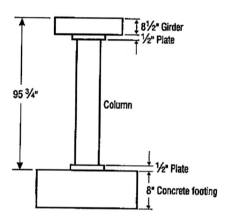

EXERCISE 17:   You work on a telephone construction crew. Your crew is installing a new section of underground telephone line. The company specifications call for one large junction box for every 200 yards of 100-pair cable, one medium junction box for every 65 yards of 50-pair cable, one medium junction box for every 10 yards of 10-pair cable, and one large junction box for each transformer. The job specifications call for 700 yards of 100-pair cable, 900 yards of 50-pair cable, 400 yards of 10-pair cable, and 4 transformers. How many junction boxes of each size are needed for the job?

EXERCISE 18:   You are the parts manager for a mobile home manufacturer. Each week you must place an order with the purchasing agent for the plumbing parts needed for the following week. Next week the factory is going to produce 32 Dakotas, 19 Trentons, 40 Belaires, and 2 Conastogas. The plumbing parts needed by each of these models are given in the following table. How many of each part should you order?

	Y-joints	T-joints	Feet of ABS pipe
Dakota	2	1	30
Trenton	1	0	25
Belaire	2	2	33
Conastoga	2	0	12

EXERCISE 19: You are an electrician working on a government contract for low-income apartments. The specifications call for the mains to be of 12-2 wire and the drops to be of 14-2 wire. The blueprints call for 300 feet of main plus 10 feet for each of sixteen apartments. Each apartment calls for three drops—one of 8 feet, one of 10 feet, and one of 15 feet. How much of each gage wire do you need?

EXERCISE 20: A service technician is sent to repair an air-conditioner at an address 20 miles from the company office. The technician spends two hours replacing the compressor. The wholesale price of the compressor is $160. The retail markup is 33%. There is also a 5% sales tax to be added to the retail price. Use this information to fill out the service invoice below. What is the total bill for the repair?

Weather Right Air Conditioning
Service Invoice

Parts .... _____

.... _____

.... _____

.... _____

Subtotal.. _____

5% sales tax...................................... _____

Total parts _____

Labor

_____ hours at $12.50 per hour .... _____

Mileage (one way from office)

_____ miles at $1.25 per mile .... _____

Total .... _____

Chapter 5

Estimating Answers

How to find answers that are about the right size

Prerequisites   This chapter builds on the skills taught in Chapter 4: *Learning Problem-Solving Techniques*. You will need a scientific calculator to complete this chapter.

To Master This Chapter   Read the text and answer all the questions. Complete the assigned exercises and activity. Work the problems on the chapter test at a satisfactory level.

Chapter Objectives   Working through this chapter helps you learn how to:

1. Make rough estimates.

2. Round and truncate whole numbers to a given number of digits.

3. Round and truncate decimal numbers to a given number of digits.

4. Estimate answers to problems that involve several steps.

5. Check the answers to problems to make sure they are reasonable.

INTRODUCTION

Have you ever heard the old saying, "Close counts only with horseshoes and dynamite"? Answers that are close, but not exactly right, sometimes *do* count. When you are working problems on the job, sometimes you need exact answers. At other times an answer that is close, but not exact, is good enough to do the job. Most of the time if you *begin* a problem by thinking of a *close* answer, you can recognize a mistake you might make later in your calculations.

Write down some situations in which a close answer would be all you need. Then write down your ideas about what kind of situations demand *exact* answers.

By now you have enough experience with your calculator to know how easy it is to press the wrong key by accident. For example, if you used your calculator to figure the sales tax on five bolts you bought, and the display window showed 14,500 for the tax, you might suspect that you had pressed a wrong key along the way!

Making a rough guess at the answer, or estimating, helps you recognize wrong answers on your calculator. As you make rough estimates, and as you do precision measurements, you will use the skill of rounding numbers.

MAKING ROUGH ESTIMATES

Alvis says his work crew is running short on floor tiles and his supervisor Liz asks how many tiles they have on the job. Alvis says "15 boxes." Alvis estimated the number of tiles to give Liz an *approximate* answer.

An **approximate** answer is one that is close to the true answer, but does not have to be the same as the true (or exact) answer.

Alvis gave a **rough estimate** because he knew an approximate answer was all that Liz wanted or expected.

Sometimes you estimate a number because a close (but not exact) answer is good enough for what you want to do.

How "rough" is a "rough estimate"? That depends on the situation. For example, if you've never paid someone to install a fuel storage tank, you may have no idea how much a contractor might charge. Before you decide to include this expense in your budget, you might ask a friend if it costs *one thousand dollars* or *ten thousand dollars.* You need a very rough estimate before you can decide whether or not to have the work done.

If you are deciding whether you have enough money to go to a movie, you might look at the money in your pocket and make a close estimate without actually counting every penny.

If you are estimating to see if you have enough material to finish a job, you might make a rough estimate. If you are estimating to tell a customer how much a job will cost, you would make a much more careful estimate.

Study Activity: *A landscaper plans to fill the flower bed at the entrance to an office building with daisies (as shown in Figure 1). The landscaper has seen flats of daisies in the correct size (each flat holds 24 plants) and remembers that one plant costs about 39 cents. At the garden center there is always a discount for buying a whole flat. The landscaper doesn't know exactly how much, but he guesses that it will be near "10% off." What is a rough estimate for the cost of 100 plants?*

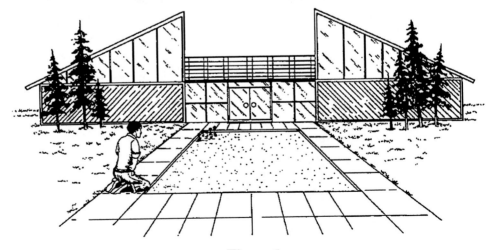

Figure 1
A rough estimate

Notice that the information given in the landscape problem is not exact. Like the landscaper, often you may need to estimate on the job when you don't have complete information.

Can you think of a way to get an estimate for the landscape problem? Try to find a method that is fast and easy for you to do in your head.

Most people can do problems in their head more easily with certain numbers such as 10, 25, 50, and 100. Perhaps that is partly because our money gives us a great deal of practice with these numbers!

≈   Different people make rough estimates in different ways, and the estimates they get will vary. Compare your rough estimate for Example 1 with the estimates made by others in your class.

Example 1:
Making a rough estimate

Estimate the answer to: 117.768 + 43.07 + 897.5.
One way to make a quick, rough estimate for the answer is to round each of the numbers to the nearest 50, 100, 150, and so on. Thus, you would round 117.768 to 100, 43.07 to 50, and 897.5 to 900. Adding 100, 50, and 900 (in your head) you would get 1,050. So your exact answer should be **roughly** the same size as 1,050. (The exact answer is 1,058.338, so your rough estimate is not too bad.)

Another way to make a quick, less-rough estimate for the answer is to round each number to the nearest 10, 20, 30 ... 100, 110, 120 ..., and so on. Thus you'd round 117.768 to 120, 43.07 to 40, and 897.5 to 900. Adding 120, 40, and 900, you'd get 1,060. (Do this, in your head, by adding 900 to 100 to get 1,000, then adding 20 + 40 = 60 to get 1,060.) You can see that this estimate—1,060—is even closer to the correct answer.

Now try Example 2 by yet a different method.

Example 2:
Estimating by truncating numbers

Make a rough estimate of the sum: 673 + 429 + 84.7 + 9.52 + 562.
Another way to do a very rough estimate is to simplify these numbers in this way: in 673, replace with zeros everything except the first 6 to get 600; in the same way, change 429 to 400, 84.7 to 80, and so on. That would give 600 + 400 + 80 + 9 + 500 or a rough estimate of 1,589. Can you tell whether your rough estimate will be higher or lower than the exact answer?

When you make a rough estimate like this, by changing 673 to 600, you are cutting off everything except the 6 and substituting zeros.

This cutting-off method of estimating is called **truncating.** ("Truncate" means "to abbreviate by cutting off.") You truncate, or cut off the 73 without taking the time to decide whether 673 is closer to 600 or to 700, so this method is quick and easy, but not very accurate. The correct answer to the sum in this example is 1,758.22, so you can see that the estimate of 1,589 is rough indeed.

To see the difference between the method of estimating in Example 1 and the method of truncating in Example 2, try Example 1 again—by truncating. That is:

Estimate the answer to 117.768 + 43.07 + 897.5 by truncating.

In Example 1, the estimates for the answers were 1,050 and 1,060. How much different is your estimate by truncating? Why are they so different? Which method is more accurate?

Now practice estimation in the following problems:

Study Activity:

- *The map tells you that it is 423 miles from Central City to Greenville. You know that, with mixed town and freeway driving, you can average about 50 miles per hour. You are in Central City and need to be in Greenville by noon. Make a rough estimate of what time you should leave.*

- When you are doing addition in your head, look for easy combinations that add to ten, such as 1 + 9, 6 + 4, or 7 + 3. These make the mental arithmetic faster. Try this in the next problem.

Find a rough estimate for the sum: 9.1 + 6.2 + 3.0 + 4.4 + 7.2.

When you estimate to get an approximate answer, you often do this by **rounding** numbers. You often round numbers, but you may not call it "rounding." Whenever you say an amount or number is "about" so big, you are rounding. Rounding numbers in mathematics is not done the way the illustration in Figure 2 seems to indicate.

The next section explains how to round numbers.

CORD Workforce Mathematics 1

Figure 2
Rounding numbers? ?

ROUNDING WHOLE NUMBERS

To talk about rounding whole numbers, we have to use the *names* for the decimal places to the **left** of the decimal point.

Figure 3 shows the names of the four decimal places to the **left** of the decimal point.

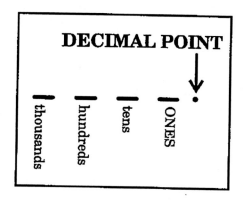

Figure 3
Decimal place names

You probably use rounded numbers when you talk about prices. For instance, you might say that the price of a new hand-held digital tachometer is "about $250" or the price of a used car is "about $5,500."

Rounding numbers is a skill that is used in many situations. For instance, a lab technician may make precise measurements in a laboratory, use a formula and a calculator to get an answer, and then round the answer. The examples here begin with rounding whole numbers. Once you know how to round whole numbers, the process for other numbers is very similar.

How might you round the whole number $2,938 to the **nearest thousand** dollars? You may be able to do that one in your head, but let's look at several methods that will work for you when you **can't** do the rounding in your head.

First, think about the following statement:

Just as all words are made from 26 letters of the alphabet, all the numbers you write are made from these ten digits: 0, 1, 2, 3, 4, 5, 6, 7, 8, 9.

The whole number $2,938 is made of the *digits* 2, 9, 3, and 8. Now, look at Example 3.

Example 3:
Rounding to the nearest thousand

Round $2,938 to the nearest thousand.
Rounding to the nearest thousand is the same as asking this question: "Is $2,938 closer to $3,000 or to $2,000?" Notice that either way all the digits to the right of the thousands place will be zeros. Figure 4 shows the key numbers 2,000, 3,000, and 2,938 on a number line. By looking at the numbers on the number line, you see quickly that 2,938 is much closer to 3,000 than to 2,000.

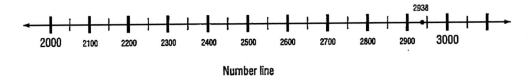

Number line

Figure 4
Using a number line to round numbers

In addition to the use of a number line, the following steps can help you round numbers to a given place—such as tens, hundreds, or thousands. Again, try rounding $2,938 to the nearest thousand. Follow the steps.

Step One

Underline the digit in the place to which you want to round.

In this example, the digit in the thousands place (see Figure 3) is 2, so you underline that digit.

$2,938

Step Two

Think—"My final answer is going to have zeros in all the places to the right of the underlined digit." **Circle** all the digits to the right of the underlined digit—those that will be replaced by zeros in the final answer.

$2,938

Step Three

Draw an arrow pointing to the digit just to the **right** of the underlined digit. **Decide** whether the digit the arrow points to is more or less than five.

$2,938
↑

In this step you are testing whether or not the number you circled is more than *half* of the way to the next higher number in the underlined place. In this problem you are asking if 938 is more than *halfway* from 2,000 to 3,000.

Step Four

If the digit with the arrow is *more* than five, **add one** to the underlined digit. If the digit with the number is *less* than five, **don't change** the underlined digit.

In the example, the digit with the arrow, 9, is more than 5, so add one to the underlined digit 2 to get 3.

Replace all the circled digits with zeros. Your final answer is 3,000.

So, because the number 2,938 is closer to 3,000 than it is to 2,000, $2,938 rounded to the nearest thousand is $3,000. Of course, when you used the number line method in Figure 4, you got the same answer—much faster.

Study Activity: Use these same steps—or draw a number line—to round the following numbers to the nearest thousand.

1. 7,644
2. 406,342
3. 2,705
4. 14,782
5. 50,645
6. 1,498
7. 4,701

Numbers exactly halfway

Did you notice that Step Four doesn't tell you what to do if the number the arrow points to is neither more nor less than 5? If the number pointed to is <u>5</u> (<u>exactly halfway</u>) the usual rule is to round <u>up</u>—add one to the underlined digit. However, in some jobs, you may find that a different rule is used when the number pointed to is exactly halfway. Always follow the rule that's used at your place of work.

Let's summarize the steps that help you round numbers.

Step One

Underline the digit in the place to which you want to round.

Step Two

Think "My final answer is going to have zeros in all the places to the right of the underlined digit." **Circle** <u>all</u> the digits to the right of the underlined digit.

Step Three

Draw an arrow pointing to the digit just to the **right** of the underlined digit. **Decide** whether the digit the arrow points to is <u>more</u> or <u>less</u> than five.

Step Four

If the digit with the arrow is *five or more,* **add one** to the underlined digit. If the digit pointed to is *less* than five, **don't change** the underlined digit. **Replace** all the circled digits with zeros.

Now practice using these steps by completing the study activities that follow.

Study Activity: • *Round these numbers to the nearest* **hundred.**

1. 7,644		**5.** 50,645
2. 406,342		**6.** 1,498
3. 2,705		**7.** 4,701
4. 14,782		

Study Activity: • *Round these numbers to the nearest* **ten.**

1. 7,644		**5.** 50,645
2. 406,342		**6.** 1,498
3. 2,705		**7.** 4,701
4. 14,782		

Did you have trouble rounding 1,498 (Problem 6 above) to the nearest ten? Let's look at the problem again. To round 1,498 to the nearest ten, you underline the 9, circle the 8, and draw an arrow that points to the 8.

1,49⑧

Because the 8 is more than 5, you add one to the underlined 9. That gives 9 + 1 = 10. But you can't write 10 in place of the underlined 9 because the 10 takes two places! So how do you take care of this?

The question is really this: "Is 1,498 closer to 1,490 or 1,500?" Figure 5 pictures these data on a number line. Looking at the number line helps you answer the question.

Figure 5
Rounding with a nine

The figure shows clearly that 1,498 rounded to the nearest ten is 1,500. This is because 1,498 is closer to 1,500 than it is to 1,490.

This really isn't a new step. If adding one to nine in the rounding process gives you a 10, just write a zero and add one to the next place to the left. You've always done that when you added numbers anyway.

Study Activity:

Let's practice rounding numbers that have nines in them.

1. Round 7,999 to the nearest ten.

2. Round 7,999 to the nearest hundred.

3. Round 7,999 to the nearest thousand.

4. Round 9,999 to the nearest thousand.

When it doesn't make sense to include several decimal places, a rounded number may be best. For example, look at Figure 6.

Figure 6
About how much?

Example 4:
Rounding numbers on the job

Last month Bill used 20 pounds of nails on 7 jobs. This month he needs to buy nails to do one more similar job. He divides 20 by 7 on his calculator to find the nails needed. The calculator answer for 20 ÷ 7 is 2.8571428. Does it make any sense for him to ask for 2.8571428 pounds of nails?

Try using the steps for rounding whole numbers to round 2.8571428 pounds of nails to the nearest pound. First, underline the digit you want to round to and circle all the digits to the right. Then draw an arrow pointing to the first digit to the right of the underlined digit.

The digit the arrow points to—8—is more than 5. So add one to the underlined digit and replace all of the circled digits with zeros. The result is

$$3.0000000$$

All the zeros after the 3 don't tell us anything. There is no reason to keep them. So the final answer is 3 pounds of nails.

Calculators show answers to however many decimal places fit into the display window. On the job, you may need to round these decimal numbers to get a more reasonable number.

ROUNDING DECIMAL NUMBERS

The process you used for rounding whole numbers also works with numbers that have digits to the **right** of the decimal point. Figure 7 names the decimal places to the left and right of the decimal point.

Notice that the names to the left and right of the **ones** place have names that are very similar. The names to the right of the ones place end in *ths* and the names to the left of the ones place do not. That little *th* makes a big difference!

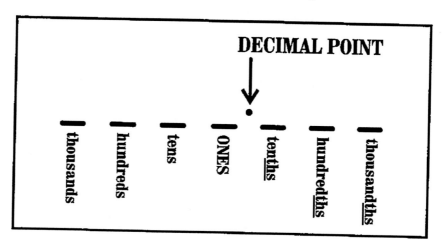

Figure 7
Decimal place names

Study Activity:

First use your calculator to add these weights. Then round your answer to the nearest pound.

4.302 lb + 34.485 lb + 83.41 lb + 102.27 lb + 20.49 lb = ?

"Round your answer to the nearest pound" is the same as saying "round to the nearest one" or "round to the nearest unit." Figure 7 reminds you that the ones (or units) place is just to the left of the decimal point.

When to round

Does it make any difference whether you first add and then round, or first round and then add? Find out by reworking the addition problem you just solved. You've already worked it by adding the numbers and then rounding to the nearest pound. Now do it by first rounding each number to the nearest pound and then adding.

Did you get the same answer both ways? Why does it matter whether you round at the beginning or at the end of a problem? What if you were adding 15 numbers instead of just five? Could that make the difference greater?

Study Activity:

Practice rounding decimals by doing the following problems. First use your calculator and then round the answer.

1. Multiply 45.7 by 99.0357 and round the answer to the nearest tenth.

2. Divide 60.80409 by 21.039 and round the answer to the nearest thousandth.

To get a more accurate answer, when you are using a calculator to work a problem, do all calculations first—without rounding—then round the final answer.

On the other hand, when you are working a problem in your head—without a calculator—it makes sense to round the numbers first, before you do a rough approximation in your head.

ESTIMATING ANSWERS TO PROBLEMS

When you work problems that involve decimals on a calculator, you might easily press a wrong key on your calculator, or put the decimal point in the wrong place. To help you recognize mistakes, do some rounding and make a rough estimate of the size of the final answer *before* you start to work a problem.

Estimating before you work a problem helps you spot your own errors so that you can correct them. Find the method that works best for you and practice estimating until you can find approximate answers quickly and easily. Try these.

Study Activity: *Estimate: 85.93 + 7.68.*

First, look for numbers that are close to 10, 100, or 1,000. To do a **rough** estimate, you could say that this problem is **about** 100 + 10. To do a closer estimate, you could add 85 and 7 (truncating to the ones place) or you could add 86 and 8 (rounding to the ones place). Either way, estimating helps you avoid a final answer that doesn't make sense!

Estimate: Subtract 56.7 from 123.9.

For this problem, one quick estimate is to think "Subtract 50 from 100; the estimate will be about 50." You would get a closer estimate by rounding to the nearest tens. Thus, 123.9 would become 120 and 56.7 would become 60. Then 120 − 60 would give 60. The actual answer is 67.2 so you can see that the second estimate is closer to the actual answer. Beginning with even a rough estimate helps you avoid answers that are not reasonable.

Estimate: Divide 129.45 by 29.067.

One quick (but rough) estimate would be 120 divided by 30, or 4. That's a close enough estimate to keep you from writing down unreasonable answers like 0.4, 40, or 400.

Estimate: 45.7 × 99.0357.

Here's one way to estimate this problem.

First, look for numbers that are close to 10 or 100 or 1,000. You might notice that 99.0357 is close to 100. Then round other numbers in a way that is easiest for you. You could just say that 45.7 is "about 50."

Second, restate the problem with your rounded numbers:

"50 times 100"

Third, work the restated problem.

Multiplying by 10, or 100, or 1,000, is easy to do in your head. If the number is a whole number, to multiply by 10, just add one zero at the right. To multiply by 100, just add two zeros at the right, and so on. Thus, $2 \times 10 = 20$ (a zero added to the right of 2). And $43 \times 100 = 4,300$ (two zeros added to the right of 43). If the number is a decimal, to multiply by 10, just move the decimal point one place to the right. To multiply by 100, move the decimal point two places to the right. Thus, $2.42 \times 10 = 24.2$ and $43.761 \times 100 = 4,376.1$.

Can you write a rule for multiplying a whole number—or a decimal—by 1,000?

Returning now to the problem of multiplying "50 times 100," think *multiplying 50 times 100 adds two zeros to the right.* Thus "50×100" becomes 5,000. The answer 5,000 gives a rough estimate to the problem 45.7×99.0357.

To make a closer estimate of 45.7×99.0357, you could truncate 45.7 to 45 and multiply 45 by 100 to get 4,500. Or you could just multiply 45.7 by 100 in your head and get 4,570, still a close estimate.

Helpful hints for estimating

Exactly how you estimate is up to you. Estimates should be fast and easy. Estimates you make before you calculate are only general guides so that you can tell if your final calculated answer is way off base.

If there are more than three numbers in a problem, you may want to round half of them *up* and half of them *down* to easier numbers. In that way, the rounding errors tend to balance each other out.

Estimating is a way to catch mistakes you may make when you press calculator keys. For this reason, it is best to do your estimating in your head. Round in any way that makes the mental arithmetic easy for you. Figure 8 summarizes the important steps you should follow **before** you do the calculations.

HOW TO MAKE A ROUGH ESTIMATE

First, look for numbers that are close to 10 or 100 or 1,000. Then round the other numbers in the way that is easiest for you. If you round one number up, try rounding the next number down. That keeps your estimate closer to the true answer.

Second, restate the problem with your rounded numbers.

Third, work the restated problem and write an estimated answer. Include the units appropriate on the answer (pounds, miles, years, or whatever).

Finally, calculate and then compare your final answer to the estimate you made at the beginning. If they are very different, estimate again and redo your work.

Figure 8
Making a rough estimate

Study Activity: *Follow the procedure outlined in Figure 8 to do the following:*

1. Divide 70.40508 by 56.073.

2. Multiply 1.23 by 9,786.

3. Carry out this operation $(45.6 \times 3.08) + 789.034$.

CHECKING FOR REASONABLE ANSWERS

You can work a mathematics problem as an exercise in a book, or you can think of the problem as a real situation involving real people, real money, real time, and objects you can touch. When you think of mathematics problems only as numbers on a page, any old answer may be as reasonable as any other—it's all just numbers anyway. This kind of thinking may lead you into wild guesses and careless mistakes.

If you make a habit of thinking of mathematics problems as related to the real world, you have a better chance of coming up with correct answers—answers that make sense.

To relate a problem on paper to the real world, use your imagination. Imagine a TV scene that the problem describes. Make the words create pictures in your mind. Imagine some real person, thing, or situation that happened to you that is like what is happening in the problem.

Before you work the problem, ask yourself "What kind of answer to this problem makes sense?" Use your rounding skills to make a rough estimate of the answer. Be sure to include the units so that you won't give an answer of 5 miles when you mean 5 hours.

BEFORE   AFTER

Figure 9
Estimate before—compare answers after

After you work the problem, ask yourself "Is my answer reasonable in this real situation?" Compare your answer to the rough estimate you made at the beginning. Think "Is my answer close to the estimate? Do I have the correct units on my answer?"

As you do the following study activity, practice using your imagination to picture a real situation.

Study Activity:

Write down a rough estimate (with units) for each problem. Then work the problem and use your estimate to make sure your answer is a reasonable one. If it isn't, check your estimate and redo the problem. Write both your original estimate and your final answer on your paper.

1. Tina has a 15-pound sack of ¼"-20 hex nuts. She wants to know approximately how many nuts are in the sack. She finds out from the manufacturer's specs that each nut weighs about 0.052 pound. Find out how many nuts—rounded to the nearest one—she has.

2. The shipping weight of a computer is 18 pounds. What is the shipping weight of 32 computers, rounded to the nearest hundred pounds?

3. A technician reported that over a 9-day period, Machine A produced 3683 fasteners. What was the average daily output of the machine, rounded to the nearest hundred?

SUMMARY

Often you estimate on the job when you don't have complete information. If you are estimating to see if you have enough material to finish a job, you may make a rough estimate. If you are estimating to tell a customer how much a job will cost, you may make a much more careful estimate.

Different people make rough estimates in different ways, and the estimates they get will vary. Try to find a method that is fast and easy for you to do in your head.

One way of rounding numbers for estimates is called **truncating.** This method is quick and easy, but not very accurate. Another way is to round numbers to the nearest ten (14.1 becomes 10, 18.3 becomes 20, 178.5 becomes 180, 1,053 becomes 1,050) and then carry out the estimation.

Steps to help you round numbers:

Step One

Underline the digit in the place to which you want to round.

Step Two	**Think** "My final answer is going to have zeros in all the places to the right of the underlined digit." Circle all the digits to the right of the underlined digit (the ones that will be replaced by zeros in the final answer).
Step Three	**Draw an arrow** pointing to the digit just to the **right** of the underlined digit. **Decide** whether the digit the arrow points to is **more or less than five.**
Step Four	If the digit with the arrow is *five or more,* **add one** to the underlined digit. If the digit pointed to is *less than five,* **don't change** the underlined digit. **Replace** all the circled digits with zeros.

Calculators generally give answers to 9 or 10 decimal places. On the job, you may need to round these long decimal numbers to get a more reasonable number.

To get a more accurate answer, when you are using a calculator to work a problem, do all calculations **before** you round the final answer.

On the other hand, when you are working a problem in your head without a calculator, it makes sense to round first before you do a rough approximation in your head.

Estimating before you work a problem helps you spot your own errors so that you can correct them. Find the method that works best for you and practice estimating until you can find approximate answers quickly and easily.

If you make a habit of thinking of mathematics problems as related to the real world, you have a better chance of coming up with correct answers—answers that make sense.

Before you work the problem, ask yourself "What kind of answer to this problem makes sense?" Use your rounding skills to make a rough estimate of the answer. Be sure to include the units.

After you work the problem, ask yourself "Is my answer reasonable in this real situation?" Compare your answer to the rough estimate you made at the beginning. Think "Is my answer the right size? Do I have the correct units on my answer?"

PRACTICING THE SKILLS

Laboratory Activity

Use the mathematics skills you have learned to complete the following activity.

Activity: **Estimating distances**

Equipment

Measuring tape
Stopwatch
Calculator

Statement of problem

People estimate distances in many jobs when accurate measurements are not required. In this activity, you use two methods of estimating distances. You determine (1) your average step length and (2) your average walking speed. You then use these two measured quantities to estimate the length of a hall and the outside perimeter of your building.

Procedure

a. Measure and mark off a 100-foot length in a hallway or on a nearby sidewalk. Begin at one end of the marked-off section and step off the distance. Walk with steps that are comfortable and normal. **Do not use unusually long or short steps.** Count the number of steps needed to cover the 100-foot distance. Record the number of steps needed to travel the 100-foot distance on a data sheet. Repeat this procedure two more times. You may get a slightly different number for each of the three tries. If so, add the three numbers and divide by three. This is your *average number of steps*. Now divide 100 feet by the average number of steps. Round this number to the nearest tenth of a foot. This is your *average step length*. Record this value on your data sheet.

b. Using the same length of 100 feet, find the **time** (in seconds) required for you to walk the 100-foot distance. Walk at a normal, comfortable pace; not unusually fast or slow. Repeat this procedure two more times and find the *average time required to travel the 100-foot distance*. Divide 100 feet by the *average time required to travel the 100-foot distance*. Round this number to the nearest tenth of a foot per second. This is your *average walking speed in feet per second*.

Multiply your average walking speed in $^{ft}/_{sec}$ by 60 $^{sec}/_{min}$ to get your average walking speed in $^{ft}/_{min}$. Record the value on your data sheet.

c. Now use this information to help you estimate the length of the hall outside your classroom. First, step off the distance walking just as you did when you determined your average step length in Step **a.** Count the steps. Round the number to the nearest whole step if necessary. Then multiply the number of steps by the average step length you determined in Step **a.** This is your estimate for the hall length. Record this value on your data sheet.

d. Repeat the estimate above by finding the time required to walk the length of the hall outside your classroom. Be sure you walk at the same speed you did in Step **b.** Round this time to the nearest tenth of a minute and multiply by your *average walking speed* in $^{feet}/_{min}$. Compare your results with others in your class. This is another estimate for the hall length. Record this value on your data sheet.

e. When measuring longer distances, timing the walk is easier than counting the steps. It's easy to lose count of the steps. Estimate the outside perimeter—distance around your building—by timing a walk around the building. Walk close to the building and at the same speed you did in Step **b.** Round the time to the nearest tenth of a minute and multiply by the *average walking speed* in $^{feet}/_{min}$. This is an estimate of the building perimeter. Record this value on your data sheet.

f. Based on the information you've gathered above, estimate how long it would take you to walk 10 miles. Do the calculations on your data sheet.

STUDENT EXERCISES

You can solve the exercises that follow by applying the mathematics skills you've learned. The problems described here are those you may meet in the world of work.

Note: *Use the techniques you've learned for estimating to solve the problems that follow.*

EXERCISE 1: You work in the shipping department for a manufacturer. You are filling a customer's order for several small items. The items ordered weigh 21 ounces, 23 ounces, 18 ounces, and 7 ounces. The policy of your company is to use a stronger box to ship products totaling more than 3 pounds. Knowing that 16 ounces is one pound, estimate whether you should use the stronger box.

EXERCISE 2: The weight capacity of a certain pallet storage rack is 18,000 pounds. Out of the following, which would probably be a safe load?

    a. 6 cartons weighing 3,162 pounds each

    b. 19 cartons weighing 879 pounds each

    c. 32 cartons weighing 612 pounds each

    d. 21 cartons weighing 933 pounds each

EXERCISE 3: #8 common nails are on sale at $0.93 a pound. The sack of nails you are buying weighs $9\frac{1}{8}$ pounds.

    a. Estimate what the nails will cost.

    b. Use your calculator to find out how much the cashier will charge you. How will the cashier round the fractional cents?

EXERCISE 4: The pricing for many small manufactured items is given in dollars per carton of one hundred. For example, a carton of 100 $\frac{5}{16}$" × 3" hex lag screws sells at a price of $9.89 per carton.

    a. What would be the price of one lag screw, rounded to the nearest penny?

b. Suppose lag screws were priced "per lag screw" instead of "per carton of 100." If the price per screw increased one penny (for example, from 10¢ each to 11¢ each), what would be the increase in **cost per hundred screws?**

EXERCISE 5: The actual annual production total at a manufacturing company was 46,293 items. What will the town newspaper report as the production total if it rounds the actual production to the nearest thousand?

EXERCISE 6: A contractor is putting down forms for two sides of a 55-foot sidewalk. The contractor uses 2" × 6" × 8' boards for the forms.

a. How many 8-foot boards are needed to line the sidewalk?

b. Estimate how much the boards will cost, if each one costs $8.95.

EXERCISE 7: You currently earn about $60 a week from a part-time job. The management has announced a 4.5% raise for all employees.

a. Estimate how much increase you can expect in each week's pay.

b. About how much will this increase your annual (52 weeks) pay? (Assume you will work roughly the same hours all year.)

c. Use your calculator to obtain exact answers to the above questions. (Round your answers to the nearest whole dollar.)

EXERCISE 8: Each bay in Warehouse #1 can hold 9 pallets, and each pallet can hold 24 boxes. The warehouse manager reports that all but 83 of the 1,200 bays are full. Approximately how many boxes—to the nearest thousand—are stored in the warehouse?

EXERCISE 9:   A board 112 inches long is used to make 10-inch braces.

a. Estimate how many braces can be cut from the board.

b. Use your calculator to find the exact answer. Round your answer to the nearest whole number of braces.

c. Is your estimate higher or lower than the exact answer?

EXERCISE 10:   You are wallpapering a 12-foot-long wall. The wall is 9 feet high, and without doors or windows. The solid-colored wallpaper you've selected is 27 inches wide and comes in 16-foot rolls.

a. Estimate how many widths of paper it will take to cover the wall.

b. Use your calculator to determine how many widths it will take.

c. Use your calculator to determine the exact total length of paper you will need.

d. How many rolls of wallpaper must you buy to get this total length?

e. Does it make any difference whether you round the number of rolls up or round it down?

EXERCISE 11:   You work in an industry that uses tape measures marked off in tenths of inches. A specification calls for a measurement between $16\frac{3}{16}''$ and $16\frac{5}{16}''$. What lengths—when rounded to the nearest tenth of an inch—can you measure with your tape that will fall within the specified lengths?

EXERCISE 12:   You install solar heating systems. The number of panels needed depends on the amount of living area and the climate. For mild climates, you take 10% of the living area to find the total area of solar panels needed. Each solar panel is 3 ft × 7 ft, or 21 ft².

a. What is the total surface area of solar panels needed for a single-story house with 1,360 ft² of living area?

b. Because of the design of the panels, you need to always have pairs of panels together. How many 21-ft^2 solar panels should you recommend to obtain this surface area and have an even number of panels?

EXERCISE 13: You are contracted for a roofing job. You estimate that you need about 4,800 roofing nails. According to a handbook, the roofing nails you need count out at about 189 nails per pound.

a. Estimate how many pounds of nails you need.

b. If you want to add 10% allowance for losses, about how many additional pounds will you need to buy? (Round to the nearest half-pound.)

EXERCISE 14: You work as a technician setting light cycles for traffic signals. You find that 85 vehicles travel down a certain street every 10 minutes and pass through the intersection. The traffic light goes from green to yellow, to red, and back to green, every 75 seconds. That's called a **cycle.**

a. Find the number of light cycles that occur every ten minutes.

b. About how many vehicles pass through the light during each cycle?

EXERCISE 15: You work in an automotive service department installing car batteries. A certain brand comes in three lengths: 8^{15}⁄$_{16}$", 10", and 12". The racks the batteries are stored on (lengthwise) are 8 feet long. For each size of this brand of battery, how many can you store on a rack?

EXERCISE 16: You need to pour a concrete slab that is to be ⅑-yard thick (that is, 4 inches), 8 yards wide, and 20 yards long.

a. How many "yards" (cubic yards) of concrete do you need? (**Hint:** Volume is calculated by multiplying the thickness by the width by the length.)

b. The cement company will take orders for only whole "yards" of concrete. How many "yards" of concrete should you order?

EXERCISE 17: Your electric bill arrived today and you want to check the amount. It shows that your previous meter reading was 77,495 (kWh) and the current reading is 79,484 (kWh). Your electric company charges $0.0759 per kWh for electricity used.

a. Estimate how much electricity you used this month.

b. Use your estimated usage to estimate what the actual bill will be.

c. What is your exact cost for electricity this month? (Round up to the nearest cent.)

EXERCISE 18: You work as a quality control inspector at a beverage factory. The assembly line you monitor produces about 20,000 bottles in a 24-hour period. You sample about 90 bottles an hour and "red-tag" the line if the reject level of your samples exceeds 2%.

a. About how many bottles are being produced each hour by the assembly line?

b. What percent of the hourly production do you sample? (Round your answer to the nearest percent.)

c. How many rejects should you allow before red-tagging the line?

EXERCISE 19: A company packages 100 paper clips into each box. You work as a quality control inspector. By weighing the clips in a box, you can check whether the packaging machine is putting the correct number of clips into each box. One hundred paper clips (without the box) should weigh 63.6 grams.

a. How much should each paper clip weigh, rounded to the nearest hundredth of a gram?

b. About how much would the clips in a box weigh, rounded to the nearest 0.1 gram, if there were 101 clips in it? If there were 99 clips in it?

c. You weigh the clips from several boxes. You record the weights as follows: 63.5 grams, 63.6 grams, 63.7 grams, 63.2 grams, 64.3 grams, 63.0 grams, 64.4 grams, 63.6 grams, 64.9 grams, and 62.9 grams. How many of these boxes should you suspect have more (or less) than 100 paper clips in them? (Notice that some small variation in the weight of the clips is expected.)

EXERCISE 20:   A belt-driven exhaust fan is being designed. As shown in the sketch below, the motor is to have a 2" pulley, and the fan a 6" pulley. The centers of the two pulleys will be separated by about 30 inches. The circular distance around a pulley (the circumference) can be computed by multiplying the pulley diameter by the number 3.142 (known as "pi"). Estimate the total length of the belt needed to turn the exhaust fan.

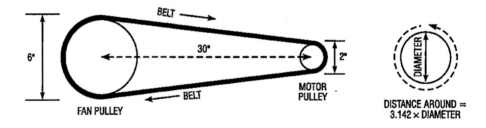

Chapter 6

Measuring in English and Metric Units

How to measure in English and metric systems of units
and use measurements to solve problems

Prerequisites   This chapter builds on the skills taught in:

Chapter 4: *Learning Problem-Solving Techniques*
Chapter 5: *Estimating Answers*

To Master This Chapter   Read the text and answer all questions. Complete the assigned activities and exercises. Work the problems on the chapter test at a satisfactory level.

Chapter Objectives   Working through this chapter will help you to learn to:

1. Use the common measurement units for length, area, volume, capacity, and weight in the English system.

2. Use the common measurement units for length, area, volume, capacity, and weight in the metric system.

3. Convert measurement units from one form to another and carry out calculations that involve various measurement units.

4. Read measurements made with common measuring tools.

5. Use tools to measure quantities and solve problems that involve these measurements.

LEARNING THE SKILLS

INTRODUCTION

In almost every job, workers need answers to questions such as these:

How long or how far is it? How long is the board? How wide is the paper? How far is it to the next town?

How much is there? How much weight? How much liquid? How much pressure? How much voltage? How much temperature?

To find answers to these questions, you *measure*—length, distance, weight, area, volume, pressure, voltage, temperature, and so on. You can use a variety of *instruments* to measure different quantities. Look at Figure 1 and see how many measuring instruments you recognize. Can you tell what quantity each one measures?

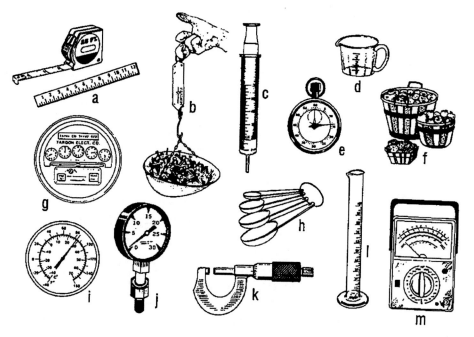

Figure 1
Instruments that measure

Measure the length of your pencil with a ruler and write down how long the pencil is. The ruler, in this case, is the **instrument** you choose to measure the length. Did you measure in *inches or centimeters*? These two units represent different ways to express a measure of length.

There are two widespread systems of measurement for common quantities such as length, weight, and capacity. You are probably most familiar with the *English system* of measurement. It's the most common system used in the United States. In it, *length* is measured in inches, feet, yards, or miles. *Weight* is measured in ounces or pounds, and capacity is measured in cups, quarts, or gallons. In most other countries in the world, people measure with the *metric system*. In it, *length* is measured in meters, *weight* is measured in grams, and *capacity* is measured in liters. Figure 2 shows some of the more common units used in each system.

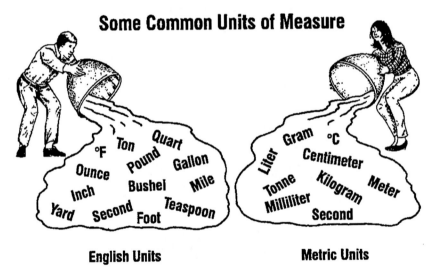

Figure 2
Common units in English and metric systems

Because the United States does more and more business with other countries, the metric system is increasingly important to us. For example, an automobile mechanic now keeps two sets of tools—one for foreign-made cars and new American cars, and one for older American cars that were made with English measurements.

Sports events such as track and field, swimming, and diving now often use metric lengths instead of feet, yards, and miles.

ENGLISH SYSTEM OF MEASURE

How tall are you? How much do you weigh? How much coffee did you drink at breakfast this morning?

You probably give your height in *feet* and *inches*, your weight in *pounds*, and the amount of coffee in *cups* (or parts of a cup). These measurements—feet, inches, pounds, and cups—are part of the **English system** of measurement.

The English system of measurement grew out of the way people measured for themselves. People measured shorter distances on the ground with their feet. They measured building supplies with their forearms, palms, and fingers. They measured longer distances by their paces (a "mile" was a thousand paces). They measured capacities with common household items such as cups, pails, and baskets. Our word gallon comes from an old name for pail. A *bushel* was a way to measure grain—and still is!

Because people, cups, pails, and baskets were likely to be of different sizes, the amount that each would measure was different. But craftsmen and merchants needed *standard* measures that were the same for everybody. In time, each common measure came to have *one* certain length, weight, or capacity that was accepted by everyone. Figure 3 shows how some of the common English measures of length developed.

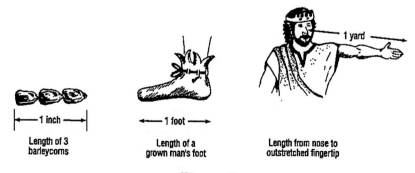

Figure 3
Where common measures of length came from

Figure 4 lists the common English units for measuring length, weight, and capacity (the amount a container holds) and tells how similar measures compare.

Length	Capacity
12 inches (in.) = 1 foot (ft)	3 teaspoons (tsp) = 1 tablespoon (tbsp)
3 ft = 1 yard (yd)	16 tbsp = 1 cup (c)
5280 ft = 1 mile (mi)	8 ounces (oz) = 1 c
	2 c = 1 pint (pt)
	2 pt = 1 quart (qt)
	4 qt = 1 gallon (gal)

Weight
    16 ounces (oz) = 1 pound (lb)
    2000 lb = 1 ton

Figure 4
Common English units

Many people know the units listed in Figure 4 by memory. These are the units that occur frequently. You need to know these if you want to take a standard vocational test for a license or certificate.

Using a unit conversion ratio

Sometimes you need to convert from one unit of measure to another similar one. For example, how many inches are in two feet? How many yards are in 1320 feet?

Two simple facts of mathematics give you a powerful way to change from one unit of measure to another similar one.

First, you know that *any number divided by itself equals 1*:

$$\frac{6}{6} = 1 \qquad \frac{3.91}{3.91} = 1 \qquad \frac{5201}{5201} = 1$$

It is easy to see that each of these fractions equals 1 because the numerator and denominator are the same. However, any quantity divided by itself equals 1 *even if the numerator and denominator are written differently*. Look at the following ratios:

$$\frac{1 \text{ ft}}{12 \text{ in.}} = 1 \qquad \frac{16 \text{ oz}}{1 \text{ lb}} = 1 \qquad \frac{4 \text{ c}}{1 \text{ qt}} = 1$$

In each case, the numerator and denominator of the ratio name the *same* amount. In each case, the ratio is equal to **one.** Let's refer to such fractions—or ratios—as **unit conversion ratios.** As we will see, they are useful in changing—or converting—from one unit of measure to another.

The second mathematical fact that helps you change from one unit of measure to another is this: *Multiplying (or dividing) by 1 does not change the value of a number:*

$$5 \times 1 = 5 \qquad 2.78 \times 1 = 2.78 \qquad \tfrac{1}{2} \times 1 = \tfrac{1}{2}$$

Follow the next example to see how you can use these two mathematical facts to convert from one unit of measure to another.

Example 1:
Converting
inches to feet

Convert 24 inches to feet with the help of the unit conversion ratio

$$\frac{1\ foot}{12\ inches}$$

You can multiply 24 inches by the number 1 without changing its value:

$$24 \text{ inches} \times 1 = 24 \text{ inches}$$

But look what happens if we replace the number 1 by the special unit conversion ratio ¹ ᶠᵒᵒᵗ/₁₂ ᵢₙ𝒸ₕₑₛ:

$$24\ inches \times \frac{1\ foot}{12\ inches} = \left(\frac{24 \times 1}{12}\right)\left(\frac{\cancel{inches} \times foot}{\cancel{inches}}\right) = 2\ feet$$

The original units (inches) divide out—since inches/inches = 1— and what is left is the desired answer in the new units—2 feet.

So 24 inches = 2 feet.

How do you pick the unit conversion ratio you need to convert from one unit of measure to another? To convert from the unit you have to the unit you want, the unit conversion ratio is always written as:

$$\frac{\textbf{new units}\ (\textit{the ones you want to change to})}{\textbf{old units}\ (\textit{the ones you have})}$$

Example 2:
Converting feet to yards

Follow the next example to see how to pick the unit conversion ratio you need for a problem.

How many yards are in 15 feet?
First, decide what the conversion is that you want to make. In this case, you want to convert *feet* to *yards:*

$$15 \text{ feet} = ? \text{ yards}$$

The old unit is *feet*, and the new unit you want is *yards*.

For the unit conversion ratio (^new units^/_old units_), you want ^yards^/_feet_. However, the *unit conversion ratio must be equal to the number 1.* So write numbers with the units to make a fraction that is equal to 1:

$$\frac{new\ units}{old\ units} = \frac{1\ yard}{3\ feet} = \frac{1\ yd}{3\ ft}$$

(If you cannot remember—or don't know—the conversion numbers between the units you are converting, you can always refer to conversion tables. In this case, for example, you can look back at Figure 4 and see that 1 yard = 3 feet.)

Now you are ready to multiply 15 feet by the unit conversion ratio ^1 yd^/_3 ft_ to get the length in yards.

$$15\ feet = \frac{15\ ft}{1} = \frac{1\ yd}{3\ ft} = \left(\frac{15 \times 1}{1 \times 3}\right)\left(\frac{\cancel{ft} \times yd}{\cancel{ft}}\right) = 5\ yd$$

15 feet is the same as 5 yards.

If you do not know the relationship of the new unit to the old unit directly, you can use more than one unit conversion ratio to convert from the old unit to the new one. Example 3 shows you how.

Example 3:
Using more than one unit conversion ratio

How many cups are there in one gallon?
The table in Figure 4 does not tell the relationship of cups and gallons. However, it *does* tell the relation of cups to quarts (4 cups = 1 quart) and quarts to gallons (4 quarts = 1 gallon). Therefore, the unit conversion ratios—in terms of new units/old units—are (^4 qt^/_1 gal_) and (^4 c^/_1 qt_). Notice that we

change first from gallons to quarts and then from quarts to cups. Thus we can change from gallons to cups as follows:

$$1\,gal = \frac{1\,gal}{1} \times \frac{4\,qt}{1\,gal} \times \frac{4\,c}{1\,qt} =$$

$$\left(\frac{1 \times 4 \times 4}{1 \times 1 \times 1}\right)\left(\frac{\cancel{gal} \times \cancel{qt} \times c}{\cancel{gal} \times \cancel{qt}}\right) = 16\,c$$

Study Activity:

- *Try writing the correct unit conversion ratios for the following problems:*

    1. Write the unit conversion ratio that converts feet to miles.

    2. Write the unit conversion ratio that converts tons to pounds.

    3. Write the unit conversion ratio that converts quarts to cups.

- *Use unit conversion ratios to make the following conversions:*

    4. Convert 6,600 feet to miles.

    5. Convert 3 tons to pounds.

    6. Convert 6 quarts to cups.

Conversion table

If your work involves making one kind of conversion over and over again, you usually have a **conversion table** so that you can look up the answer you need.

For example, in the building trade, leveling land and measuring distances are often done with *decimal parts of a foot* (24.62 feet, for instance). However, the building plans may be given to carpenters and masons in *fractions of an inch* (for instance, 24 ft 7½ in.). Builders often use a conversion table, similar to the one shown in Figure 5, to convert between fractions of an inch and decimal parts of a foot.

Fractions of an inch

Inches	0"	⅛"	¼"	⅜"	½"	⅝"	¾"	⅞"
0"	0.00	0.01	0.02	0.03	0.04	0.05	0.06	0.07
1"	0.08	0.09	0.10	0.11	0.12	0.14	0.15	0.16
2"	0.17	0.18	0.19	0.20	0.21	0.22	0.23	0.24
3"	0.25	0.26	0.27	0.28	0.29	0.30	0.31	0.32
4"	0.33	0.34	0.35	0.36	0.38	0.39	0.40	0.41
5"	0.42	0.43	0.44	0.45	0.46	0.47	0.48	0.49
6"	0.50	0.51	0.52	0.53	0.54	0.55	0.56	0.57
7"	0.58	0.59	0.60	0.61	0.62	0.64	0.65	0.66
8"	0.67	0.68	0.69	0.70	0.71	0.72	0.73	0.74
9"	0.75	0.76	0.77	0.78	0.79	0.80	0.81	0.82
10"	0.83	0.84	0.85	0.86	0.88	0.89	0.90	0.91
11"	0.92	0.93	0.94	0.95	0.96	0.97	0.98	0.99

Figure 5
Conversion table
Converting fractions of an inch to decimal fractions of a foot

Whenever you convert—whether you look up the answer in a table or calculate it—remember to also *estimate* the answer so that you can decide if you converted correctly.

You can use the table in Figure 5 to convert inches to decimal parts of a foot, *and* you can use it to convert decimal parts of a foot to inches. The next examples show you how.

Example 4:
Using a conversion table

Convert 4⅝ inches to hundredths of a foot.
First, locate 4 inches in the first column (under *Inches*).
Then, staying in the **same** row, go over from 4 to the column labeled ⅝ and read 0.39 as the answer.

4⅝ inches = 0.39 foot

Is this answer reasonable? 4⅝ inches is a little more than one third of a foot. The decimal 0.39 is a little more than a third. Yes, the answer is reasonable.

Convert 0.45 foot to inches.

First, locate 0.45 in the body of the table.

Next, look *across* the row 0.45 is in to the column on the far left (the one labeled *Inches*) to find the number of inches in 0.45 foot. In this case, 0.45 is in the row for 5 inches. (Place a piece of paper or straightedge under the line of numbers to help you read across the table accurately.)

Then, look *up* the column, from 0.45, to the top to find the additional fraction of an inch needed. In this case, 0.45 is in the column for ⅜ inch.

0.45 foot = 5⅜ inches

Is the answer reasonable? 0.45 foot is almost half of a foot, and 5⅜ inches is almost half of a foot. Yes, the answer is reasonable.

Study Activity: *Use the conversion table to make these conversions.*

1. Convert 9⅜ inches to a decimal part of a foot.

2. Convert 0.23 foot to inches.

3. Convert 7 feet 8 inches to feet (expressed in decimal form).

4. Convert 5 feet 3⅞ inches to feet (expressed in decimal form).

5. Convert 3.81 feet to a number in feet and inches—such as 2 feet 5½ inches.

METRIC SYSTEM OF MEASURE

Do you ever buy 3-liter bottles of soft drink? Have you noticed that the speedometers on automobiles have numbers for miles per hour *and* kilometers per hour? Have you noticed that packaged food items are labeled with the weight in ounces *and* grams? These measures—liters, kilometers, and grams—are part of the metric system of measure.

The metric system was created about two hundred years ago by a group of French scientists to simplify measurement. In the metric system, each of the common kinds of measure—length, weight, and capacity—has *one* basic unit of measure. Length (or distance) is measured with *meters,* weight and mass are measured with *grams,* and capacity is measured with *liters.* To measure smaller amounts, **you divide the basic unit into parts of ten, a hundred, or a thousand, and so on.** To measure larger amounts, **you multiply the basic unit by ten, a hundred, or a thousand, and so on.** To convert, then, you either multiply or divide by 10, 100, 1000, and so on. Such calculations are easy to carry out.

Today, almost every country in the world uses the metric system as its standard of measure. The United States is the only major country in the world that still uses the traditional English system of measure. Even England has changed to the metric system, which is why the *English system* of measure is now often called the *U.S. system* of measure.

Nevertheless, within the United States, scientific work and much manufacturing is done with metric measurements. You can expect to encounter both English *and* metric measurements in your work.

Metric units of measure

Length, in the metric system, is measured in *meters.* A meter is just a little longer than a yard. A football field is about 90 meters long.

Weight is measured in *grams.* An ordinary metal paper clip weighs about one gram. A nickel, or 5-cent coin, weighs about 5 grams. Most packaged foods in the United States are now labeled with both pounds and grams. A one-pound box of powdered sugar, for example, weighs about 454 grams.

Capacity—how much a container can hold—is measured in *liters.* A liter is just a little more than a quart. You can buy two-liter and three-liter bottles of soft drinks at the grocery store.

Just as the English system divides feet into smaller units called inches and multiplies feet into larger units such as yards and miles, the metric system divides and multiplies its basic units. However, in the metric system, the units are divided and multiplied by ten, hundred, thousand, and so on.

You can tell how a measure compares to a meter, gram, or liter by the prefix used with it—such as **kilogram**:

Kilo	means	thousand (1000)
Hecto	means	hundred (100)
Deca	means	ten (10)

The prefixes kilo, hecto, and deca make the basic unit *larger*. A **kilo**meter is a thousand meters. A **hecto**gram is a hundred grams. A **deca**liter is ten liters.

Deci	means	one-tenth ($\frac{1}{10}$)
Centi	means	one-hundredth ($\frac{1}{100}$)
Milli	means	one-thousandth ($\frac{1}{1000}$)

The prefixes deci, centi, and milli make the basic unit *smaller*. (To help you remember which prefixes make the unit smaller, notice that all these prefixes end in the letter *i*.) A **deci**gram is one-tenth of a gram. A **centi**meter is one-hundredth of a meter. A **milli**liter is one-thousandth of a liter.

People measure with some metric units more than others. You most often see the basic units coupled with the prefixes *kilo* and *milli*.

Figure 6 lists the common metric units for measuring length, weight, and capacity and tells how similar metric measures compare. It also gives you a general comparison between metric units and English units. For example, one inch and one centimeter are different in length (if you have a ruler with both scales, you can see that a centimeter is shorter than an inch). However, both are used to measure short lengths. Likewise, miles and kilometers are used to measure long distances.

Common metric measures

Length
> 1 kilometer (km) = 1000 meters (m)
> 1 centimeter (cm) = 0.01 meter (m)
> 1 millimeter (mm) = 0.001 meter (m)

Weight
> 1 kilogram (kg) = 1000 grams (g)
> 1 milligram (mg) = 0.001 gram (g)

Capacity
> 1 milliliter (mL) = 0.001 liter (L)

Metric measures compared to English measures

Length
> kilometer—little less than a mile; measure long distances
> meter—little longer than a yard; measure mid-distances
> centimeter—less than an inch; measure small distances
> millimeter—small fraction of an inch; measure small distances with greater precision

Weight
> kilogram—little over two pounds; weigh amounts over about 2 pounds
> gram—about the weight of a paper clip; weigh amounts up to about 2 pounds
> milligrams—about the weight of a few grains of salt; weigh very small amounts such as medicine dosages

Capacity
> liter—little more than a quart; measure quart- and gallon-size capacities
> milliliter—less than a teaspoon; measure teaspoon- and cup-size capacities

Figure 6
Metric measures

Study Activity: Practice measuring with metric units by carrying out the following measurements.

Measuring with centimeters:
Measure the length of your index finger with the centimeter scale on your ruler.

Next, choose another length (such as the length of your desk, the width of your textbook, the length of your foot, the distance between the buttons on your shirt, or the width of your hand). *Before* you measure the length, estimate how many centimeters long you think it is. Choose your estimate quickly, taking the first number that occurs to you. Then measure the length in centimeters. Was your estimate longer or shorter than the actual length? How close were you?

Choose several other lengths, estimate, and measure until your estimates are within 2 cm of the actual length.

Measuring with meters:

Measure the height of a door with a meter stick. Then, choose a distance, estimate its length in meters, and then measure it with a meter stick. Repeat these steps until your estimates are regularly within 1 m of the actual length. For example, you might choose the length of the room, the width of the room, the length of a window, and so on.

Measuring with grams:

Weigh your textbook on a scale marked in grams. Then, choose an item, estimate its weight in grams, and then weigh it. Repeat these steps until your estimates are regularly within 100 grams of the actual weight. For example, you might choose to weigh other books, a notebook, and other small items in the classroom.

Measuring with milliliters:

Fill a small paper cup with water. Pour the water into a measuring cup marked in milliliters (mL). Then, choose another small container and estimate how many milliliters of water it will hold. Fill the container with water and then measure the amount of water with the measuring cup marked in milliliters. Repeat these steps until your estimates are regularly within 50 milliliters of the actual amount. For example, you might choose drinking cups of various sizes, pill bottles, or any item that will hold water.

Converting metric measures

Converting from one unit to another in the English system of measure can often be complicated. However, in the metric system, conversion is as simple as moving the decimal point of a number. You need to know only *which direction* (right or left) and *how far* to move it.

You can make a chart that helps you figure out how to move the decimal point when you convert from one metric unit to another.

To make your own chart, list the prefixes, *in order from left to right* and *without skipping any prefix*, from largest to smallest. Your chart should look like this:

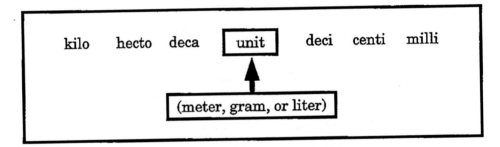

Follow the next examples to see how to use the chart.

Example 5:
Converting kilometers to meters

Convert 1.254 kilometers to meters.
If you convert from kilometers to meters with a unit conversion ratio, this is what you will do:

$$\frac{1.254 \text{ km}}{1} \times \frac{1000 \text{ m}}{1 \text{ km}} = 1254.0 \text{ m}$$

The number of kilometers (1.254) and the number of meters (1254) differ only in the position of the decimal point. The decimal point in the number 1254.0 is *three places to the right* of the decimal point in the number 1.254.

Look at the names in the chart you made:

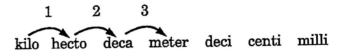

The name *meter* is *three places to the right* of the name *kilo.*

Thus in converting from kilometers to meters, all you have to do is move the decimal point in the number for kilometers three places to the right.

Example 6:
Converting milligrams to kilograms

Convert 50,281 milligrams to kilograms.
To convert with unit conversion ratios, you have

$$50{,}281 \text{ mg} = \frac{50{,}281 \text{ mg}}{1} \times \frac{1 \text{ g}}{1000 \text{ mg}} \times \frac{1 \text{ kg}}{1000 \text{ g}} = \frac{50{,}281 \text{ kg}}{1{,}000{,}000} = 0.050281 \text{ kg}$$

The number of milligrams (50,281) and the number of kilograms (0.050281) differ only in the position of the decimal point. The decimal point in the number 0.050281 is *six places to the left* of the decimal point in the number 50,281 (remember, if the decimal point is not shown, it is to the *right* of the digits). On the chart, kilo is *six places to the left* of milli:

$$6 \quad 5 \quad 4 \quad 3 \quad 2 \quad 1$$

kilo hecto deca gram deci centi milli

To use the chart to convert from one metric unit to another, count the number of places *from* the old unit *to* the new unit. Move the decimal point of the number you want to convert the *same number of places* in the *same direction* (right or left). The new number is in the new unit.

Example 7:
Using the conversion chart

Use the chart to convert 358 millimeters to centimeters.
First, find milli and centi on the chart:

$$1$$

kilo hecto deca meter deci centi milli

Count the number of places *from* milli *to* centi and notice if it is to the right or left. In this case, centi is *one place to the left* of milli.

Move the decimal point in 358 *one place to the left*. The new number is in the new unit:

$$358 \text{ mm} = 35.8 \text{ cm}$$

Study Activity: *Use the chart—or unit conversion ratios—to make the following conversions:*

1. Convert 17.35 kilometers to meters.

2. How many grams are in 34.83 kilograms?

3. Convert 0.075 hectoliter to liters.

4. How many milliliters are in 15 liters?

5. Convert 156 centimeters to meters.

Converting between English and metric measures

Usually you will do a job in either English units or metric units, but not both. Sometimes, however, you need to convert units not only within one system, but from one system to the other. The chart in Figure 7 tells how measures compare between the two systems.

Metric to English	English to Metric
Length	*Length*
1 mm = 0.04 in.	1 in. = 2.54 cm
1 cm = 0.39 in.	1 ft = 30.48 cm = 0.305 m
1 m = 39.37 in. = 3.28 ft	1 yd = 0.914 m
1 m = 1.09 yd	1 mi = 1.609 km
1 km = 0.62 mi	
Weight	*Weight*
1 g = 0.035 oz	1 oz = 31.103 g
1 kg = 2.2 lb	1 lb = 0.453 kg
Capacity	*Capacity*
1 mL = 0.2 tsp	1 tsp = 5 mL
1 L = 1.057 qt	1 c = 237 mL
	1 qt = 0.946 L
	1 gal = 3.785 L

Common abbreviations used above:

in. = inch	m = meter	c = cup
ft = foot	km = kilometer	qt = quart
yd = yard	oz = ounce	gal = gallon
mi = mile	lb = pound	tsp = teaspoon
mm = millimeter	g = gram	L = liter
cm = centimeter	kg = kilogram	mL = milliliter

Figure 7
Comparison between English and metric measures

Study Activity: *Use the information in Figure 7* *to create the unit conversion ratios you need to make the desired conversions:*

1. Find how many gallons are in a 3-liter bottle of cola.

2. You are constructing a fence 100 meters long. How many yards of fence will you construct?

3. A plumbers' solder syringe is listed as size 14.7 grams. How many ounces is this? Round to the nearest tenth ounce.

4. Two towns are 35 miles apart. How many kilometers separate them?

5. A piece of paper is 0.1 mm thick. How many inches thick would a stack of 100 sheets be?

MEASURING WITH INSTRUMENTS

When you need to know the measure of a quantity—such as how long is the board, how wide is the paper, how high is the temperature, or what's the air pressure—you measure. Most often, you measure with an instrument designed for the task. When you use a measuring instrument, you need to know these things:

- What the instrument measures
- Units in which the instrument measures
- How to use the instrument
- How to read the measurement from the instrument

As you work through the remainder of this chapter, make sure you know how to work with any instrument you need.

---

*You can find a more complete table of information for creating unit conversion ratios in the Table of Conversion Factors in Appendix A at the end of this text.

Measuring length

Study Activity:

If you needed to measure the length of a piece of metal, you probably would reach for a ruler and measure the length without giving it much thought. However, if you were explaining how to measure with a ruler to someone who had never used a ruler, what would you tell them? Answer the first four questions in the next exercise as if you were explaining how to use a ruler.

1. What does a ruler measure?

2. What is the unit of measure for the ruler with which you most often measure?

3. Tell how to place a ruler on a piece of metal to measure the length of the metal. Where do you put the beginning mark of the ruler? Where do you place the marked edge of the ruler?

4. Explain how to read the measurement (length of the dark bar) in the following cases. The unit on the ruler is *inches*.

   a.

   b.
   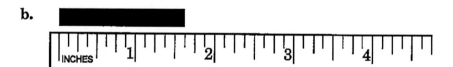

   c.
   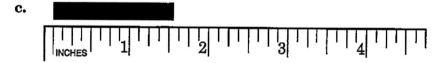

5. If you measure the length of a sidewalk to be constructed by "pacing the length," what instrument do you use? What are the units of your measure? How can you convert your measurement to feet?

Measuring length with greater precision

If you want to know the length of a piece of metal, measuring its length to the nearest ⅛ inch is probably good enough for your work. If you want to know the length of a house, finding its length to the nearest inch may be sufficient. The accuracy needed for a measurement depends upon how you plan to use the measurement.

If you work on an assembly line, in a machine shop, or some other technical-related industry, you may need to measure length with a greater degree of accuracy than can be done with a ruler. A vernier caliper, shown in Figure 8, is a tool that measures smaller distances with great precision.

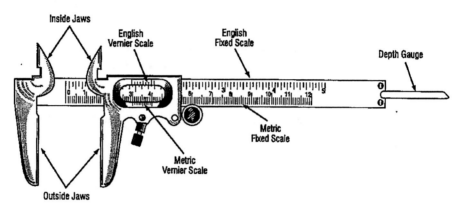

Inside Jaws

English Vernier Scale

English Fixed Scale

Depth Gauge

Metric Fixed Scale

Metric Vernier Scale

Outside Jaws

Figure 8
Vernier caliper

A **caliper** is a tool that measures distance such as the outer or inner diameter of a pipe, the length of a cut piece of metal, or any other item that can fit within the caliper jaws. A *vernier scale* is an extra measuring device that slides along the *fixed scale* to provide greater precision in the measurement.

The vernier caliper shown in Figure 8 has two fixed scales, one marked in English units and one marked in metric units. Each fixed scale has a corresponding vernier scale. When you use a tool with a vernier scale, check the scale so that you know the precision (smallest unit of measure) of the vernier scale.

Measuring with a vernier scale

If a ruler is marked in millimeters, as shown in Figure 9 below, you can measure to the nearest millimeter. The sketch shows centimeter (distance between numbers) and millimeter (smallest marked interval) units. You can see that there are 10 millimeters in one centimeter.

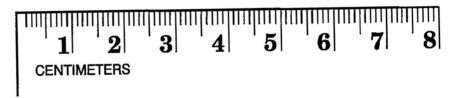

Figure 9
Part of a metric ruler

Suppose, however, you want to measure to the nearest *tenth* of a millimeter. The manufacturer of the ruler cannot add ten marks between each millimeter mark because the marks would run together. A manufacturer *can*, however, add a vernier scale to the ruler that might look like the one shown in Figure 10.

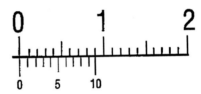

Figure 10
Comparison of units on the fixed scale and vernier scale

The distance from the 0 mark to the 10 mark on the vernier scale shown in Figure 10 is equal to 9 mm—as seen on the fixed scale. The vernier scale distance is divided into ten parts. Each part then is 0.9 mm long—or 0.1 mm short of 1 mm. Because the distances between adjacent marks on the vernier scale are a *tenth of a millimeter* less than 1 mm, the vernier caliper is able to measure distances to the **nearest tenth of a millimeter.** The **precision** of the instrument (Figure 10) is then one tenth of a millimeter.

How do you read a vernier caliper? Look at Figure 11. There, a vernier caliper is shown measuring the outside diameter of a pipe. The blowup below the figure shows a larger view of the vernier window.

To read a vernier caliper:

• First find the millimeter mark on the fixed scale that is just to the left of the 0 mark on the vernier scale. From the blowup, you can see that it's the 3.5-cm mark. That's because the 0 mark on the vernier scale is located somewhere between the 3.5 and 3.6 marks on the fixed scale. That tells you that the diameter of the pipe is greater than 3.5 cm but less than 3.6 cm.

• Second, look along the ten marks on the vernier scale and the millimeter marks on the adjacent fixed scale, until you find the **two** that **most nearly line up.** In the blowup of Figure 11, the 7th mark on the vernier scale most nearly lines up with one of the millimeter marks on the fixed scale.

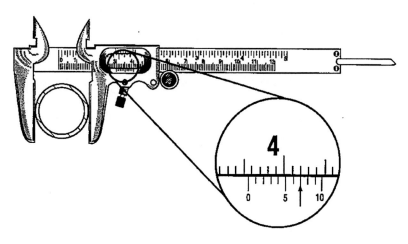

Figure 11
Reading a pipe diameter with a vernier scale

• Third, to get the correct reading for the pipe diameter, simply add the digit 7 to the end of 3.5 to get 3.57. The correct pipe diameter, to a tenth of a millimeter or a hundredth of a centimeter, is 35.7 mm or 3.57 cm.

Now let's go through another example, similar to this one, just to practice the steps one more time.

Example 8:
Reading measurements with a vernier scale

Read the outer diameter of the pipe to the nearest tenth of a millimeter. The vernier scale shown below measures to the nearest tenth of a millimeter.

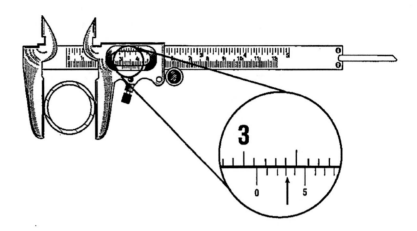

First, locate the millimeter mark on the fixed scale just to the left of the 0 mark on the vernier scale. Read the fixed scale to be 3.1 cm.

Next, look for the mark on the vernier scale that most nearly lines up with a mark on the fixed scale. It helps here to estimate how far the 0 mark on the vernier scale is from the last millimeter mark on the fixed scale. In the drawing, the 0 mark points to a position that is *less than half* the distance to the next millimeter mark. You can expect, then, for the marks to line up somewhere below the fifth vernier-scale mark. In the example, the *third* vernier-scale mark lines up most nearly with a fixed-scale mark. That fits the estimate.

Because the *third* vernier-scale mark lines up best, the extra distance from the 3.1-cm mark is 0.3 *mm* (three times the precision of the vernier scale, which in this case is 0.1 mm). Add the two values together:

$$3.1 \text{ cm} + 0.3 \text{ mm} = 3.1 \text{ cm} + 0.03 \text{ cm} = 3.13 \text{ cm}$$

The outer diameter of the pipe is 3.13 cm or 31.3 mm.

Study Activity: *Read each of the following measurements to the nearest tenth of a millimeter—or hundredth of a centimeter.*

1.
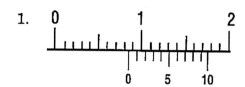

2.
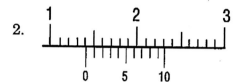

3.
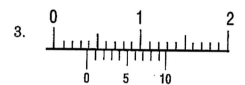

Measuring temperature

You may be able to tell the general temperature of an item by touching it. With your hands, you routinely decide if something is too hot, too cold, or just about right. When you need to know the *measure* of temperature, you use a thermometer.

Thermometers are marked with one of two common scales for measuring temperature. In the United States, temperature is most often measured in **degrees Fahrenheit** (°F), named for the German physicist who created the scale. In terms of the Fahrenheit scale, water freezes at 32°F and water boils at 212°F. The temperatures between those two measurements are divided into 180 equal parts. Each part is one Fahrenheit degree. Fahrenheit temperatures you are familiar with include the following: 100°F (a hot day), 0°F (a cold day), 98.6°F (body temperature of a healthy person).

The other common scale for measuring temperature is **degrees Celsius** (°C), named in honor of the Swedish astronomer who created the scale. (Before 1948, the scale was officially called *degrees centigrade*; you may occasionally encounter that name for the scale.) The Celsius scale is often used in scientific work. Countries that use metric measurements use the Celsius scale. In terms of the Celsius scale, water freezes at 0°C and water boils at 100°C. The temperatures *between* those two measurements are divided into one hundred equal parts. Each part is one Celsius degree. On the Celsius scale, 38°C is a hot day, –18°C is a cold day, and 37°C is the body temperature of a healthy person.

Figure 12 shows two different styles of thermometers. Each is marked with both degrees Fahrenheit and degrees Celsius. For the liquid-in-glass thermometer on the left, the *top* of the column of liquid (usually mercury) shows the temperature. For the dial thermometer on the right, the marker points to the temperature.

Study Activity: *Write the answers to the following questions on your own paper.*

1. Thermometers measure _____.

2. The two common scales for measuring temperature are degrees _____ and degrees _____.

3. What is the temperature, in degrees Fahrenheit, showing on the thermometer on the left in Figure 12?

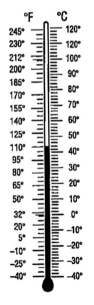

Figure 12
Thermometers

4. What is the temperature, in degrees Celsius, showing on the thermometer on the left in Figure 12?

5. What is the temperature, in degrees Fahrenheit, showing on the thermometer on the right in Figure 12?

6. What is the temperature, in degrees Celsius, showing on the thermometer on the right in Figure 12?

7. Look at the scales on the two thermometers in Figure 12. At what temperature are the degree Fahrenheit and the degree Celsius the same?

On the job, if you must convert between degrees Fahrenheit and degrees Celsius on a regular basis, you probably will have a conversion table to use. You can also convert a temperature measurement from one scale to the other with a formula. The formulas are discussed in another chapter.

SUMMARY

When you need to know the measure of a quantity—such as, how long is the board, how wide is the paper, how cold is the temperature, or how much is the air pressure—you measure.

Two common standards of measure are used to measure amounts of length, weight, and capacity. One is the English system of measure. Some common units are:

Length
  12 inches (in.) = 1 foot (ft)
  3 ft = 1 yard (yd)
  5280 ft = 1 mile (mi)

Capacity/volume
  3 teaspoons (tsp) = 1 tablespoon (tbsp)
  16 tbsp = 1 cup (c)
  8 ounces (oz) = 1 c
  2 c = 1 pint (pt)
  2 pt = 1 quart (qt)
  4 qt = 1 gallon (gal)

Weight
  16 ounces (oz) = 1 pound (lb)
  2000 lb = 1 ton

The other system of measure, used in most countries of the world, is the metric system. Some common units are:

Length
    1 <u>kilo</u>meter (km) = 1000 meters (m)
    1 <u>centi</u>meter (cm) = 0.01 meter (m)
    1 <u>milli</u>meter (mm) = 0.001 meter (m)

Weight
    1 <u>kilo</u>gram (kg) = 1000 grams (g)
    1 <u>milli</u>gram (mg) = 0.001 gram (g)

Capacity
    1 <u>milli</u>liter (mL) = 0.001 liter (L)

To convert from one measure to another similar one (for example, feet to inches, kilograms to grams, or inches to centimeters), multiply by a unit conversion ratio or use a conversion table.

Using a Unit Conversion Ratio Write a unit conversion ratio in the form ᴺᵉʷ ᵘⁿⁱᵗˢ/ₒₗd units so that the fraction equals 1. Multiply the value you want to convert by the unit conversion ratio. The answer is in terms of the new unit.

Conversion Table Some tables list a series of measurements in one unit and show the equivalent measures in another unit. To convert a measurement from one unit to another, look up the value in the table.

Converting Between Metric Units Unit conversion ratios can be used to convert from one metric unit to another. However, as you convert (for example, meters to centimeters, grams to kilograms, milliliters to liters), the only difference between the measures in the old unit and the measures in the new unit is the *placement of the decimal point*. You can use the following chart to help you decide how to move the decimal point when you need to convert:

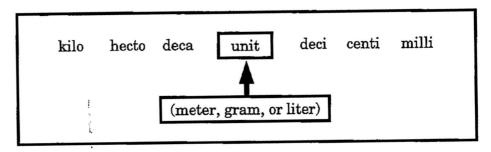

To use the chart to convert from one metric unit to another, count the number of places *from* the old unit *to* the new unit. Move the decimal point of the number you want to convert the *same number of places* in the *same direction* (right or left). The new number is in the new unit.

When you use a measuring instrument, you need to know the following:

- What the instrument measures
- Units in which the instrument measures
- How to use the instrument
- How to read the measurement from the instrument

Laboratory Activity

Use the mathematics skills you have learned to complete the following activity.

Activity **Measuring volumes**

Equipment Empty 2-liter soft drink bottle
Six empty 12-ounce soft drink cans
Measuring cup marked in ounces (1-cup or 2-cup capacity)
Funnel
Package of 8-ounce paper cups
Ruler
Water supply
Masking tape
Pencil and paper
Calculator

Statement of Problem In this activity you will compare the cost of a consumer product that is sold by a metric volume to the cost of the same product sold by an English volume. The price of a 2-liter soft drink is $1.49. The price of a six-pack of 12-ounce soft drinks is $1.89.

Procedure **a.** Calculate the cost per ounce of the soft drink in the six-pack of 12-ounce cans sold for $1.89.

b. Measure 3 inches down from the top of the 2-liter soft drink bottle (see drawing after this step). Put a piece of masking tape on the bottle so the bottom of the tape marks the 3-inch distance. Put the funnel in the bottle neck. Fill the measuring cup with water to the 8-ounce (or 16-ounce) mark and pour it into the bottle. Write a tally mark on a sheet of paper to indicate "one cup." Repeat this process until the water level reaches the bottom of the tape. Mark a tally mark for the last cup and, if water is left in the cup, write the number of ounces left in the cup. Count the number of tally marks and multiply by the 8 ounces (or 16 ounces). Subtract from this number the number of ounces of water left in the measuring cup. This is the volume of the 2-liter bottle in ounces. Save the filled bottle for Part **e.**

3 in.

Tape

2-Liter
Soft Drink
Bottle

6 UP

c. Calculate the cost per ounce of the soft drink in the 2-liter bottle sold for $1.49.

d. If an average serving size is 8 ounces, how many servings will each package of soft drink give? Which package of soft drink has the lower cost per ounce? Which is the better buy? Why do you think this is a better choice than the other one?

e. Fill the empty 12-ounce cans with water. Determine the number of 8-ounce cups you can fill from the six 12-ounce cans. How does this compare to the number of 8-ounce servings you calculated in Part **d**? Determine the number of 8-ounce cups you can fill from the 2-liter bottle you filled in Part **b**. How does this number compare to the number of 8-ounce servings you calculated in Part **d**?

STUDENT EXERCISES

You can solve the exercises that follow by applying the mathematics skills you've learned. The problems described here are those you may meet in the world of work.

Note: *Wherever possible, use your calculator to solve the problems that require numerical answers. The Table of Conversion Factors in Appendix A at the end of the text includes the unit equivalents you will need to convert from one unit to another.*

EXERCISE 1: If a paper clip weighs about one gram, approximately how many paper clips would be in a 0.5-kilogram box of clips?

EXERCISE 2: A car's fuel tank can hold 16 gallons of gasoline.

a. How many liters would it take to fill an empty tank of this capacity?

b. If gasoline were sold by the liter (as it is in most of the rest of the world) instead of by the gallon, what would be the cost of a liter of gasoline that is now priced at $1.20 per gallon? (**Hint:** Estimate this first, thinking about quarts and liters. Ask yourself, "Should a liter cost more or less than a gallon?")

EXERCISE 3: How much will the water weigh that fills a 6000-gallon storage tank that is used for fire protection? How many cubic feet of water is this? Assume water weighs about 8.3 lb per gallon and a cubic foot of water weighs 62.4 lb.

EXERCISE 4: A contractor is constructing three sidewalks and a driveway for a new home. The three sidewalks will take about 35 cubic feet of concrete each and the driveway will take another 135 cubic feet. A truck has delivered 6 cubic yards of concrete.

a. How many cubic feet of concrete will it take to construct the three sidewalks and driveway?

b. How many cubic feet of concrete did the truck deliver?

c. Will you have enough concrete to construct the sidewalks and driveway?

EXERCISE 5:   Electric utility companies measure the usage of electricity by the kilowatt-hour, rather than the watt-hour. For example, a 300-watt light bulb used for one hour would consume 300 watt-hours of electricity (300 watts × 1 hour = 300 watt-hours).

a. How many **kilowatt-hours** would the 300-watt light bulb consume while in use for one hour?

b. A manufacturer uses an electric kiln that operates at 5,000 watts for three hours a day. How many kilowatt-hours of electricity does the kiln use each day?

c. If the electric utility company charges $0.1259 per kilowatt-hour, how much does it cost to fire the kiln each day?

EXERCISE 6:   The petroleum industry uses "barrels" as a measure of volume. Each barrel is the same as 42 gallons. An oil refinery has 12 storage tanks. Each tank has an inside volume of about 33,500 cubic feet.

a. How many gallons of oil can each tank store?

b. How many barrels of oil can be stored at the refinery?

EXERCISE 7:   Insurance mortality tables are used to help companies predict how much they may expect to pay out in claims, and so how much they should charge for insurance premiums. A portion of such a table follows.

Mortality Table

Age	Death rate per 1000
⋮	⋮
28	1.93
29	1.96
30	1.99
31	2.03
32	2.08
⋮	⋮

a. If Home and House Insurance Company insures 62,142 clients who are 30 years old, how many "thousand" clients is this?

b. Find the predicted number of deaths per thousand from the table for clients of thirty years of age.

c. How many total claims can Home and House expect from their 30 year-old clients?

EXERCISE 8: Wild River Products produces camping supplies. Each tent produced requires the services of three departments, as listed in the table below.

Tent Production Time

Department	Tent Model A	Tent Model B	Tent Model C
Cutting	0.6 hr	1.0 hr	1.5 hr
Assembly	0.7 hr	0.9 hr	1.2 hr
Packaging	0.2 hr	0.2 hr	0.4 hr

a. How many minutes does each tent model spend in the assembly department?

b. What is the total production time for each tent model in hours? In hours and minutes?

c. If you were going to determine the required production time for an order of 24 Model-B tents, which would be easier to use: the times in hours and minutes, or the times in hours?

d. What is the total production time for 24 Model-B tents?

EXERCISE 9: A water chiller is installed to provide chilled water for a production factory. The water chiller has an automatic thermostat adjustable for 47°F to 55°F output. Use the dual-scale thermometer in Appendix A to express the output in degrees Celsius.

EXERCISE 10: Your new water heater's thermostat is calibrated in degrees Celsius. What setting should you use if you want a hot-water temperature of 140°F? (**Hint:** Use the dual-scale thermometer in Appendix A to determine your answer.)

EXERCISE 11: Two dial indicator gages are available: one with graduations down to 0.00005" and the other with graduations down to 0.002 mm. Which gage should you select to obtain the finer precision?

EXERCISE 12: The smallest division of a fractional-inch rule is ¹⁄₆₄ inch. The smallest division of a metric rule is 0.05 mm. Which rule will allow you to measure to the smaller graduation?

EXERCISE 13: A shop order calls for 50 aluminum slats to be cut. Each slat will be 6.4 cm wide. Each cut will waste 0.3 cm of material.

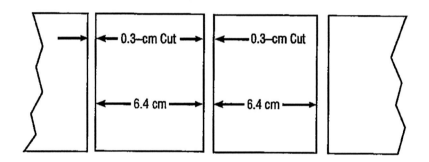

Slats to be cut from stock

a. What is the width of material needed for each slat and cut?

b. How much stock will be needed for the total order?

c. How many meters of stock is this?

EXERCISE 14: You are filling the oil reservoirs of new engines. Each engine requires 5 quarts of oil.

    a. How many gallons of oil will you need to fill 270 engines?

    b. How many 50-gallon drums of oil will you use?

EXERCISE 15: The cylinder displacement in automobiles was expressed in cubic inches in the past, but now is being reported in liters.

    a. About how many liters of displacement would a 400-cubic-inch engine have?

    b. About how many cubic inches of piston displacement would a 2.2-liter engine have?

EXERCISE 16: A measurement of the coolant in an automobile radiator indicates that it should protect down to –30°C, and that it has a boiling point of 106°C. This means that the coolant will freeze at –30°C, and boil at 106°C. (Use the dual-scale thermometer in Appendix A to determine your answers.)

    a. At what temperature in degrees Fahrenheit will the coolant freeze?

    b. How hot (in degrees Fahrenheit) will the coolant be when it starts to boil?

EXERCISE 17: To get electrical power to an air compressor, you need about 60 feet of wire. A 15-meter roll of wire is to be used.

    a. Will you have enough wire to power the compressor?

    b. How much will you lack, or how much will you have left over?

EXERCISE 18: A bolt must pass through the materials shown in the following drawing. What is the total thickness that is to be bolted?

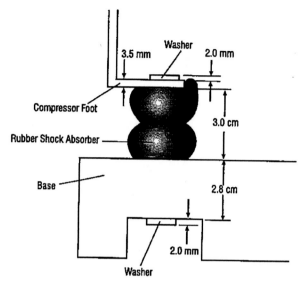

Material to be bolted

EXERCISE 19: The load limit of a flatbed truck trailer is posted at 5 tons. Several large pieces of equipment that have their weights tagged by the manufacturers have been loaded onto the truck. The tags show 4080 pounds, 350 pounds, 1590 kilograms, and 2840 pounds.

a. What is the load limit of the truck trailer expressed in pounds?

b. What is the total weight of the equipment loaded onto the truck trailer?

c. Is the trailer overloaded?

EXERCISE 20: You need to cut an 8-foot board into five equal pieces.

a. How far apart will each of the four marks be, expressed in feet, inches, and fractions of an inch, as would be found on a tape measure? (**Hint:** Use the conversion table in Figure 5.)

b. Work the problem in metric: calculate the length of the board in centimeters. How far apart will the four marks be, expressed in centimeters (as would be found on a metric tape measure)?

(This page is intentionally blank.)

Chapter 7

Using Graphs, Charts, and Tables

How to use graphs, charts, and tables to
convey information

Prerequisites   This chapter builds on the skills taught in
                                 Chapter 4: *Learning Problem-Solving Techniques*
                                 Chapter 5: *Estimating Answers*
                                 Chapter 6: *Measuring in English and Metric Units*

**To Master
This Chapter**   Read the text and answer all questions. Complete the problems and activity. Work the problems on the chapter test at a satisfactory level.

**Chapter
Objectives**   Working through this chapter will help you to learn to:

1. Read tables.

2. Read and draw bar graphs.

3. Read circle graphs.

4. Read and draw line graphs.

5. Interpolate readings on a graph.

6. Extend a line graph so you can estimate more values.

INTRODUCTION

Many people find that a picture gives them information more easily and faster than words. Most of us grasp information quickly and easily with a *picture*. Graphs, charts, and tables present numbers and other kinds of information in "picture" form. They provide us with a quicker way to understand the numbers and how they are related.

READING TABLES

As you already know, we live in a world full of numbers. We need ways to organize numbers so that we can make sense out of them. One of the simplest ways to organize numbers is to put them all together in rows or columns. When we do this, we make a **table.** Figure 1 shows several typical tables.

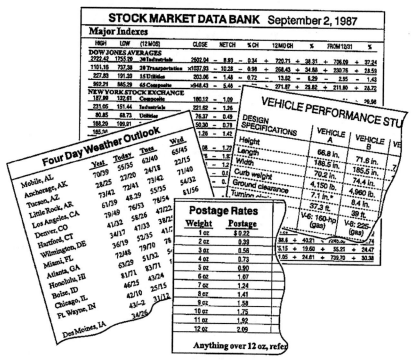

Figure 1
Tables of data

Each table shows groups of data that relate to one another. For example, look at the table titled "Postage Rates." The first column lists different weights for letters. The title above this column is labeled *Weight*. The second column lists the postage amounts. The title above this column is *Postage*. The most important fact about this table is that the data in the first column are related to those in the second column. For example, the 1-oz weight goes with the $0.22 postage, the 2-oz weight goes with the $0.39 postage, and so on. Therefore, when postal clerks look at the table, they can see the postage due on each package quickly.

Look at the table in Figure 1 with the title "Four Day Weather Outlook." It's made up partly of numbers and partly of words. The left column lists the names of certain cities. The columns to the right identify certain days of the week—*Yesterday, Today, Tuesday,* and *Wednesday.*

Tables like this are not always labeled completely. For example, to use this table, you might have to figure out that the two numbers shown together refer to the *high* and *low* temperatures for the day. Also, by looking at the pairs of numbers in the row for Los Angeles, for example, you might guess that they refer to Fahrenheit readings, not Celsius. Why? Can you tell what day of the week the table is for? Why do you think the table shows two days of "future" weather and only one day of "past" weather?

Study Activity: One of the tables in Figure 1 may be familiar to you. It is labeled "Vehicle Performance Study." Use this table to answer the following questions:

1. What is the title of the table?

2. What are the labels for each row? For each column?

3. What do the three numbers in the first row have in common with each other?

4. What do the numbers in the first column have in common with each other?

Sometimes tables of numbers are rather detailed. They can be difficult to read because there may be too many values listed. In such a case, you can use graphs—another useful way to show data. Let's see how **bar graphs** can be used to do this.

READING BAR GRAPHS

A **bar graph** is a picture of information. The same information can be listed or written in a paragraph. What does a bar graph do that a list of data or a table doesn't do? Let's look at a sample bar graph.

The first item to read in any graph is the *title* of the graph. The title gives you information about what is pictured in the graph. In Figure 2, the title is *Households with electronic appliances*. Next, what is shown on the horizontal line at the bottom? What is shown on the vertical line on the left? The labels tell us that the horizontal scale shows the *Percentage of households*. The vertical scale lists *Electronic appliances*. Then, what is the purpose of the bars? The length of a bar allows us to make comparisons.

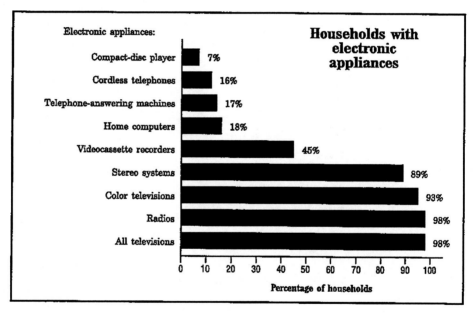

Figure 2
A horizontal bar graph

What does the length of a bar represent? Look at the label at the bottom of the graph. The length of the bar must show the percentage of households that have a particular appliance. The number at the end of the bar gives you the actual percentage.

Study the bar graph in Figure 2 and then try to answer the following questions.

1. Should automobiles be included in the list of appliances? Why?

2. How many kinds of appliances are shown?

3. What appliances are used in over half of the households?

4. What appliances are used in less than half of the households?

5. What other information do you need to find how many households have home computers?

The bar graph in Figure 2 is a *horizontal* bar graph because the bars extend from side to side. A bar graph can also have bars that extend up and down. This kind of bar graph (shown later in Figure 3) is called a *vertical* bar graph.

Let's go back to the earlier question. What does a bar graph do that a list of the information does *not* do?

A bar graph provides a *picture* of information. The picture in a graph helps us to see groups of information more quickly than we can from a list that we read. For instance, you may have noticed in Figure 2 that the top four bars are reasonably close together, the last four are very close together, and the middle bar (for VCRs) doesn't seem to fit either group. The grouping of the bars into three categories might suggest conclusions such as these:

1. Almost all households have televisions, radios, and stereo systems.

2. About half of all households have videocassette recorders.

3. Only a few households have computers, telephone-answering machines, cordless phones, or compact-disc players.

The bar graph makes it possible for you to grasp information quickly and to draw conclusions from it. Bar graphs also help you make a variety of comparisons.

Write a sentence that compares the number of households with compact-disc players to those with stereo systems.

Write a sentence that compares the number of households with color televisions to those with videocassette recorders.

Write the percent of homes that do *not* have home computers.

As you can see, the bar graph makes it easy to understand and compare information.

Figure 3 shows a *vertical* bar graph. What is the graph about? Next, look at the labels at the left side and at the bottom. Notice that the labels along the bottom show two years, 1986 and 1987. Where does 1986 stop and 1987 start?

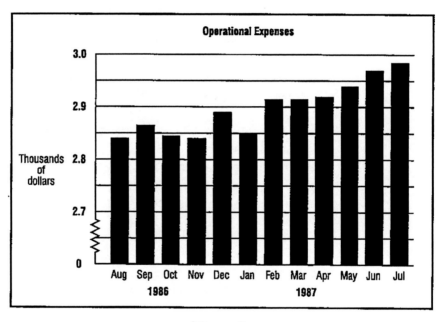

. **Figure 3**
A vertical bar graph

The label on the side says "Thousands of dollars." This means that a certain business spends thousands of dollars each month on operational expenses. However, look at the scale along the side of the graph. You can see the numbers 3.0, 2.9, 2.8, and 2.7, but where are 2.6, 2.5, and so on down to 0?

This graph shows you a handy technique that's often used on graphs with very large numbers. The scale of a graph does not always have to include "0" as a starting point. It need show only the portion of the scale that is needed to picture the data. But to avoid confusion, it is common to show that the scale leaves out a portion of the numbers, in this case, from 0 up to 2.7 thousand dollars. This allows the graph to show small differences around 2.5 thousand dollars, without having to show very tall bars going from 0 up to 2.5 thousand! Can you find the symbol that shows that some of the scale is left out?

Use the graph in Figure 3 to answer these questions.

1. Were operational expenses going up, down, or staying the same in the first part of 1987?

2. Which month had the highest operational expenses? Lowest operational expenses?

3. During which two months did operational expenses stay about the same in 1987?

Can you figure out how many thousands of dollars were spent in January of 1987? Let's go through the steps to estimate the answer. First, find the vertical bar for January of 1987. Then follow the bar up to its end. Notice that it ends at a line that is not labeled.

Second, figure out the value that belongs to this unlabeled line. Notice that, in this case, the unlabeled line is halfway between the line labeled 2.8 and the line labeled 2.9. The amount between these two lines is 0.1, so halfway would be

$$\frac{1}{2} \times 0.1 = 0.05$$

Thus the unlabeled line must be the value of the bottom line plus 0.05 or

$$2.8 + 0.05 = 2.85$$

The unlabeled line has a value of 2.85. January spending must have been 2.85 *thousand dollars*. This method of estimating a value on a graph is called *interpolation*.

CORD Workforce Mathematics 1

Study Activity: Figure out, using interpolation, what the values should be for the remaining unlabeled lines in Figure 3.

This same approach can be used to read the amounts shown by bars that end *between* two lines. Look at December spending. It's almost up to 2.9 thousand dollars. Perhaps we could estimate that it's about ¾ of the way from 2.85 to 2.9 thousand dollars. The amount between these two lines is 0.05, so ¾ of the way would be

$$\frac{3}{4} \times 0.05 \ = \ 0.0375$$

So, the height of the December bar, that is, December's spending must be

$$2.85 + 0.0375 \ = \ 2.8875 \text{ thousand dollars}$$
$$\text{or rounded, } 2.89 \text{ thousand dollars}$$

In Figure 3, use interpolation to estimate spending for April of 1987.

How to read any graph

You can get information from a graph quickly if you follow the steps given here.

First, read the *title* of the graph.

Second, read the *labels* and range of numbers (scale) along the sides.

Third, determine what *units* the graph uses.

Fourth, look for *groups, patterns,* and *differences.*

Practice these steps in the following study activity.

Study Activity: As a purchaser for fire department supplies, you are responsible for keeping a supply of dry-cell batteries for handheld equipment used by the firefighter. A trade magazine shows that some types of batteries perform better than others. The report displays a bar graph, as shown below.

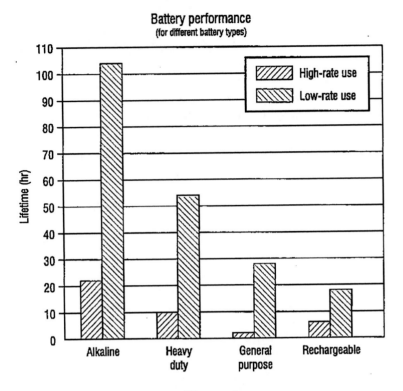

Figure 4
Charting battery performance

Based on the bar graph in Figure 4, answer these questions.

1. Which type battery lasts the longest under either high-rate or low-rate use?

2. The department is using heavy-duty batteries now. How do they compare to the other types of batteries available?

3. The fire department needs batteries in flashlights to last through a minimum of 8 hours of high-rate use. Which battery type(s) would you select to meet this requirement?

4. Under conditions requiring only occasional, low-rate use—such as portable radio gear—batteries should last at least 48 hours. Which battery type(s) would you select to meet this requirement?

5. Cost is an important factor. What does the graph say about the cost of each type of battery?

DRAWING BAR GRAPHS

To *draw* a bar graph, *follow* steps similar to those you used to read a bar graph. Now, however, *you* must decide on the labels and *you* must choose how to draw the bars.

First, decide what you are trying to show. Choose a title that describes your graph accurately.

Second, choose the general labels and range of numbers (scales) for the bottom and the left side.

Third, decide what units you want for your chart.

Fourth, draw the graph.

Choosing units

Choose your units so that your graph fits into the space you have. For example, suppose you have to present last week's production figures for your company. The data are shown below. What units would you choose to show the following information on a bar graph?

Bottles packaged each day last week

Monday	125,765
Tuesday	147,872
Wednesday	152,091
Thursday	148,286
Friday	147,100

The horizontal reference line of the graph should be labeled with units of time. In this case, that would be the five days of the week—Mon, Tues, Wed, Thurs, Fri. The horizontal reference line can also be called the horizontal axis. The axis of a graph is either the horizontal or vertical line that defines the quantities.

To choose the units for the vertical reference line of the graph, find the smallest and largest values of bottles packaged. This is the range of values that your data represent. If your axis was labeled from 0 up to 150,000 bottles, the five bars would all be about the same height.

Instead of showing bars that are all about 150,000 units tall, you can leave out a portion of the scale. To do this, you should start with a value slightly smaller than the smallest value (125,765) and end with a value just above the largest (152,091). Indicate—with the proper symbol—that some values are left out, as was done in Figure 3. The vertical reference line can also be called the vertical axis.

The plural of axis is axes. As you have just seen, axes are used in making graphs. Generally, one of the axes is a horizontal line—often called the x-axis—and the other is a vertical line—often called the y-axis. The horizontal and vertical axes form a 90° angle and thus are perpendicular to each other.

Also, you should draw between 5 and 10 lines to estimate the units on the vertical axis. You decide to use 120,000 bottles as the smallest number and 160,000 bottles as the largest number. This includes all the data. It also allows you to use an interval of 10,000 bottles, a convenient number to work with, and lets you draw just 5 lines—for 120,000, 130,000, 140,000, 150,000, and 160,000.

So, to make a bar graph of the data above, leave out the scale from 0 up to 120,000 bottles. Indicate this on the graph with the broken-line symbol. Then draw and label the lines that represent 120,000 bottles, 130,000 bottles, 140,000 bottles, 150,000 bottles, and 160,000 bottles. This way, when you draw the bars, they will end at different points and clearly show the differences between each day's production.

Here are some hints to help you select a scale for bar graphs.

1. Find the largest and smallest values you need to show.

2. Imagine how near to each other the ends of the bars will be if you start the scale of the axis at zero and continue up to the largest value. If they end up with nearly the same height, it may be better to start near the smallest value, and show that some values are left out.

3. Intervals of 5, 10, 50, 100, 1000, and so on make it easier to estimate values from the graph. Try to pick an interval so that you will have only 5 to 10 lines to draw.

Drawing a vertical bar graph

As you go through the following example, draw a vertical bar graph to picture the information provided.

Example 1:
Graphing the number of self-employed workers

The total number of self-employed workers has increased since 1980. In 1980 there were 8.6 million self-employed workers; in 1986 there were 9.3 million. The Bureau of Labor Statistics estimates that there will be 10.7 million self-employed workers in the year 2000.

First, what is this paragraph about? What is a good title for the bar graph that will show this information? Write a title for the data on your own paper, and make a table of the data with two columns—one for the year and one for the number of workers. Fill in the table with the data.

Second, what labels will you use? The *time* periods are usually drawn along the line at the bottom of the graph. What label goes there for this example? Write the labels for the bottom and the left side of the graph. The title you used for your table may help you decide what labels to use.

Third, look at all the information in the table. What is the gap between the years? What is the *smallest* number of self-employed workers in your table? What is the *largest* number?

Remember that you can "squeeze" lots of numbers into a **broken scale** that starts at zero. You do this when you want to show clear differences between bar lengths at the top of the bars.

Fourth, draw the two axes (the bottom horizontal reference line and the left vertical reference line) beginning in the lower left corner of your paper. Think about the minimum value you choose, and the highest number in the table. Indicate a broken scale if you use one. Decide how many horizontal reference lines you need. Then sketch in the bars and labels.

If you don't like the way your bar graph looks, or if it doesn't fit in your space, rethink some of your decisions. You may want to change some of the labels, too. Then draw your final version.

When to use a bar graph

The information pictured in Figure 2 indicated one fact (*percentage of households*) about several different things (*various appliances*). The information pictured in Figure 3 indicated one fact (*amount of operational expenses*) over several different times (*months*). The information in Figure 4 indicates two facts (*hours of high-rate use* and *hours of low-rate use*) for *four different batteries*.

A bar graph is good for showing one or two facts about several things, or for showing one or two facts over several time periods. When you want to show changes over time, a vertical bar graph works best, with the time periods labeled across the bottom.

A bar graph is easiest to read when there are not very many bars. If you have more than 12 bars, another kind of graph or chart may be better. **Bar graphs work best when you have only three to seven groups of information to compare.**

READING CIRCLE GRAPHS

A **circle graph,** like a bar graph, is a picture of information. A circle graph usually shows how a *whole* is made up of *several parts*. The whole is the complete circle, like a whole pie. Each part is a slice of the pie. Some people refer to circle graphs as "pie charts."

Each part in a circle graph is shown as a percentage of the whole. The whole circle represents 100%, and each slice shows a part of 100%. Together the percentages (the slices) add to 100% (the whole pie).

Not all percentage information can be shown as a circle graph. Look back at Figure 2. The facts in that graph are percentages, but they are not parts of a whole.

Use a circle graph when you can picture your information as a whole pie (100%) divided into slices. Figure 5 shows a circle graph about types of treatment at Morgan Clinic.

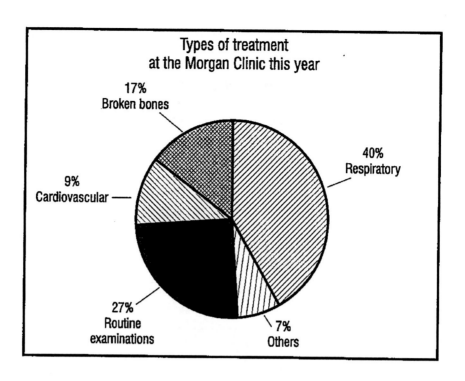

Figure 5
A circle graph

To read the circle graph in Figure 5, practice the steps you've learned for reading charts and bar graphs.

First, read the *title* of the graph.

Second, read the *labels*.

Third, figure out what *units* the graph uses. In a circle graph the units are often percentages, or parts of a whole.

Fourth, look for *groups, patterns,* and *differences.* For this circle graph, compare the sizes of the slices.

Notice that this circle graph shows what happened at the clinic for one year **and it does not show changes over time.** Use the circle graph in Figure 5 to answer the questions in the following study activity.

Study Activity:

1. What kind of treatment was provided most often at the Morgan Clinic during the year?

2. Compare the number of *cardiovascular treatments* to the number of *routine examinations*. Do this by writing on your paper the number that correctly fills the blank in this statement: *There are about _____ times as many routine examinations as there are cardiovascular treatments.*

3. Rank the types of treatment given at the clinic this year, starting with the most frequent, down to the least frequent.

A circle graph helps you compare parts of a whole to each other and to the whole. Often a circle graph shows how money—represented by parts of a dollar—is spent. Figure 6 shows such a circle graph.

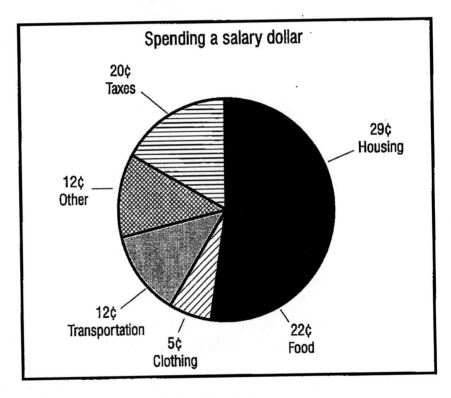

Figure 6
A circle graph for money

Use the circle graph shown in Figure 6 to answer the questions in the study activity that follows.

Study Activity: 1. What category of spending consumes most of the dollar?

2. What category of spending is almost equal to *Taxes*?

3. What fraction of a dollar do housing and food **together** consume?

Another way of presenting information is to use a pictograph. In the pictograph of Figure 7, information is presented on the production of microchips at several different locations.

Use the graph in Figure 7 to answer the questions that follow.

IN THE CHIPS

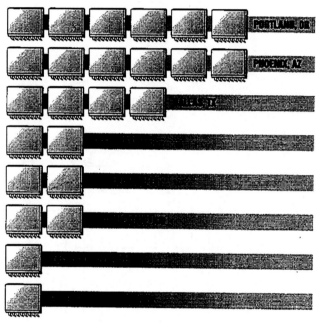

Each microchip above represents a major semiconductor plant.

Figure 7
A pictograph

Study Activity: 1. Which city has the most semiconductor plants?

2. Which state has the most semiconductor plants?

3. How many semiconductor plants are in Portland?

4. Phoenix has approximately 4800 workers in their semiconductor plants. What is the average number of workers in each plant?

READING LINE GRAPHS

You have seen how bar graphs and circle graphs are used to display information. Another common type of graph is a **line graph.** A line graph shows values of data over a certain range, by displaying the data as points on a graph that make up a line or a curve.

You may have seen thermometers that are labeled with both Celsius and Fahrenheit temperature scales. On these thermometers, you can read the temperature in degrees Fahrenheit or in degrees Celsius. But what if your thermometer has only one temperature scale, and you need the other? What if you want to know how the Fahrenheit and Celsius temperature scales are related? You might look for a table that has a matching list of Fahrenheit and Celsius temperatures. Or you might use a conversion formula to calculate the value you need. Another way is to use a line graph. Figure 8 shows a line graph that relates Celsius and Fahrenheit temperatures.

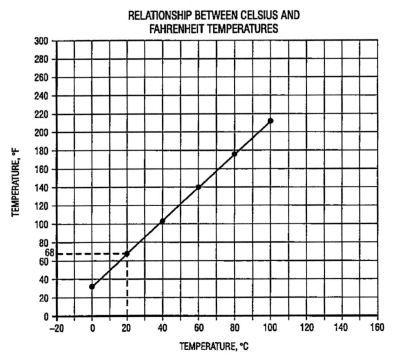

Figure 8
Line graph of Fahrenheit and Celsius temperatures

To figure out what the graph contains, first look at the labels. What temperature scale is shown on the bottom axis? What temperature scale is shown on the side axis?

Notice how a line graph differs from bar graphs and circle graphs. You can see that the information is not shown with bars, or sections of a circle, but rather with little "dots." Notice that the dots are used to form a **line** that shows how the temperatures are related. It is this **line** that gives the graph its name—*line graph*. You can see in Figure 8 that the line slopes up, from left to right. This means that for low Celsius temperatures, you can expect low Fahrenheit temperatures—and for high Celsius temperatures, you can expect correspondingly higher Fahrenheit temperatures.

As mentioned, data points on a line graph are connected by lines. These lines provide us information on the *trend* of the data. For instance if the line goes from left to right and up, the *trend* is for the quantity on the x-axis to increase as the quantity on the y-axis increases. However, if the line connecting two data points goes from left to right and down, the *trend* is for the quantity on the x-axis to increase as the quantity on the y-axis decreases. In the first case, we say that the slope of the line is positive and in the second case the slope is negative. Thus the slope is a measure of how the data being graphed are changing. This change is called a *trend*.

The line graph in Figure 8 is like a table of data. Each dot on the line represents equal Celsius and Fahrenheit temperatures. Let's use Figure 8 to figure out some equivalent temperatures.

Example 2:
Reading a temperature conversion graph

What Fahrenheit temperature corresponds to 20°C?

Look at the bottom axis of the graph in Figure 8—the Celsius temperatures. Find the place on the axis that represents 20°C. From here, go straight up until you reach the graphed line. There should be a dot there. From that dot go straight left to a location on the vertical axis—the corresponding Fahrenheit temperature. What is the Fahrenheit value represented by this point on the vertical axis? The point on the vertical axis may not be a labeled point. In this case, you need to estimate the value, using the adjacent temperature values that are shown. What did you get? Did you get about 70°F? (The correct value is 68°F.) Did you use interpolation to estimate the temperature?

What Celsius temperature corresponds to 32°F?

You can also read a line graph the "other way." Look at the vertical axis of the graph. Find the place on the axis that represents 32°F. From here go straight to the right, until you reach the line graph. There should be a dot there. From the dot on the line graph, go straight down until you reach a point on the bottom axis—the corresponding Celsius temperature. What is the Celsius value at this point on the axis? Did you get a value of 0°C? Is that what you expected?

What if you want to read a temperature that is not shown with a dot? That's when the line drawn through the dots can help you. The line shows that the dots follow a trend, and if enough dots were plotted, they would all be on this line. Whenever you use the line to estimate values in between the plotted values (dots), you are **interpolating** between the data. Let's interpolate between the graphed data to find a temperature not shown by a dot.

What Fahrenheit temperature corresponds to 50°C?

As before, find the place on the horizontal axis that corresponds to 50°C. Then go straight up until you meet the graphed line. This time you don't find a plotted point—or dot—on the line. However, since the line is drawn, you can *assume* that a dot is there. From this point, go straight to the left, as before, until you reach the side axis. What is the Fahrenheit temperature that you find? Did you get a little bit more than 120°F?

What about temperatures that are beyond the values shown on the graph?

Sometimes you need values that are beyond those shown on a graph. You would like to be able to **extend** the graph, relying on the trend shown by the graph. This is called **extrapolating,** or **extending,** the graph. *Extending* a graph normally requires some understanding of how the data on the graph are related. In the case of Fahrenheit and Celsius temperatures, you probably already know that they are related by a simple formula. So you know that the relationship or trend shown will continue for higher and higher Celsius and Fahrenheit temperatures (as well as for lower and lower ones). You could sketch in what you expect the graph to look like by extending the line that is already drawn.

For example, suppose you need to know what Fahrenheit temperature corresponds to an oven temperature of 150°C. On a worksheet, trace the graph shown in Figure 8, leaving room on the right and above. Now use your ruler to extend the line graph on your paper beyond the value corresponding to 150°C on the horizontal axis. Then, using the procedure for reading the graph, find the temperature in degrees Fahrenheit that equals a temperature of 150°C. Did you get about 300°F?

In Figure 8, the horizontal and vertical axes were already labeled out far enough to allow you to extend the graphed line. Sometimes, you will have to extend these axes, too, so you can know how far to extend the line—and what value to read from the graph.

Now let's consider an example of a line graph, where the relationship is better pictured by a *curved line* than a straight line.

Example 3:
Reading a graph of changing pipeline pressure

Figure 9 shows a line graph of how the pressure in a high-pressure pipeline changes from morning to afternoon on a certain day. Notice the label on the side of the graph. It tells you the values of pressure that are plotted on the graph.

The data are plotted with dots and joined with a line. Notice that the line is a curved line. When you look at this graph, you can compare the afternoon value with the morning value and see that the pipeline pressure is getting lower.

PIPELINE PRESSURE

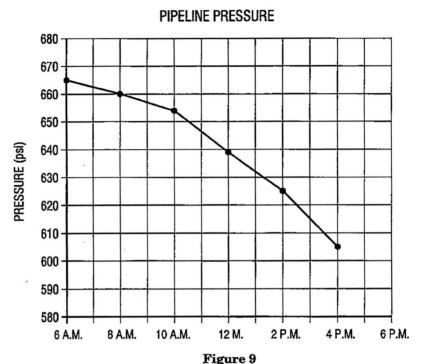

Figure 9
Line graph of changing pipeline pressure

You can also see that the pressure is dropping faster in the afternoon than in the morning. We can tell this because the line becomes increasingly steeper as the day progresses. Line graphs are particularly useful in showing these types of changes in the quantities or trends. This is especially true for line graphs with "time" on the horizontal axis.

Line graphs—whether straight or curved—show trends in the plotted data.

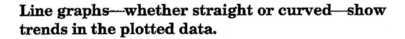

You can read values from the curved line in Figure 9, just as you did with the temperature conversion graph. You may wonder what happened to the pressure between 10 A.M. and 12 M. The plotted points tell what the pressure was at 10 A.M. and at 12 M. Can you determine what the pressure was at 11 A.M.? As before, you must **interpolate** to find the answer. The curved line indicates that the pressure at 11 A.M. was somewhere between the values at 10 A.M. and 12 M., perhaps "648." Does that seem reasonable?

Look again at Figure 9. Suppose you wanted to know what the pressure was going to be at 6 P.M. Can you **extend** this graph out to 6 P.M.? How confident would you feel about the value you determined by extending the graph?

Example 4:
Reading a graph of inventory and sales data

Controlling an inventory is important in a sales business. Consider the following example. A particular company experienced a rapid growth in sales. As a result, for a certain period, inventory in the warehouse declined. Soon, however, the manufacturing plant was able to increase output and restore the inventory levels. The graph in Figure 10 shows both the sales and inventory during this time.

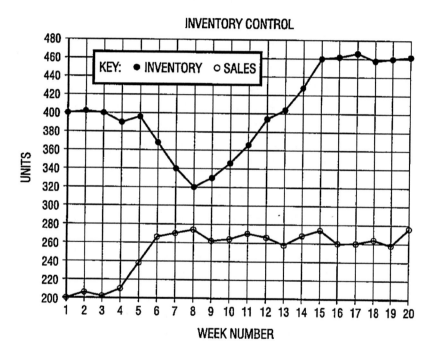

Figure 10
Line graph of inventory and sales

It is common to see line graphs that show more than one graphed quantity—as in Figure 10. Usually, the purpose of such graphs is to show the relationship between the two quantities. When more than one quantity is shown, there must be some way to tell which line corresponds to which quantity. This is done with a **key.** Can you find the key on this graph?

The key in Figure 10 tells you that one symbol is used to indicate the **inventory data** and another is used to show the **sales data.** In this graph, what is graphed by the top line—the inventory data or the sales data?

Figure 10 shows that during the first few weeks inventory was kept to about **200 units above** the number of units sold. You can look at the lower line and see that the increase in sales took place during weeks 5 and 6, after which sales remained fairly steady. But notice what happened to the inventory during this time. Did the inventory stay the same, increase, or decrease?

You should be able to see from the graph that, when sales increased, inventory decreased. In fact, it almost decreased to the point that the warehouse had only as many units on hand as were sold each week. Apparently, this company was not expecting such an increase in sales. It took several weeks for inventory to "catch up" to the level of nearly **200 units above** the number being sold per week. Look at the graph and see if you can tell how many weeks it took for inventory to stabilize after the beginning of the sales increase in week 5.

DRAWING LINE GRAPHS

You will probably have many occasions to draw line graphs. Follow these steps to draw a line graph:

First, decide what you are trying to show. Choose a title that describes your graph accurately.

Second, choose the general labels for the axes. It may be helpful to arrange your information in a table first, to see clearly what you want to graph.

Third, figure out what units you want for your graph. Draw your axes. Mark and label them with the units you've selected.

Fourth, by going over and up from the origin, plot the points for your graph.

Fifth, begin at your first point and draw a line through the remaining points that best represents the data you've drawn. The line may be straight or curved, depending on the relationship between the values you are graphing.

As an example, go through these steps to draw a graph of how electrical current in a circuit changed when the voltage changed.

Example 5:
Graphing electrical readings

Here is a table of information for an electrical circuit.

Electrical readings for a circuit

Voltage (volts)	Current (amperes)
0	0
10	1
20	2
30	3
40	4
50	5

Use one of the line graphs you've already seen in the chapter to help you set up your graph. Look at the table of numbers you are going to plot to help you decide what title and labels to use for this graph.

Next, draw the axes on a sheet of graph paper. Write your title and your labels. Using regular spacing along the axes (you should be able to use the lines printed on the graph paper), mark the volts along the bottom, 0, 10, and so on, up to 60, and the amperes at the left, 0, 1, and so on, up to 5.

Now you are ready to plot the points in the table. To plot the first point in the table, 0 volts giving 0 amperes, begin at the origin and go 0 units over and then 0 units up. Of course you didn't go anywhere! The origin is the first point on your line graph. Make a small dot at the origin to show that you have graphed these values as the first point.

To plot the second point in the table, 10 volts giving 1 ampere, begin at the origin and go over to 10 along the horizontal axis. Then from there go 1 unit straight up. Make a small dot at that point.

To plot the third point, begin at the origin, go over to 20 and then up to 2. Make a dot to show the third point of your line graph. In the same way, plot the fourth, fifth, and sixth sets of data.

Now use a ruler, or a straightedge, to draw a line that joins the first point to the second point, and the second point to the third, and so on.

This particular graph is a **straight** line. Is the line you drew a straight line? If it isn't, plot the points carefully again. Compare your graph to the one shown in Figure 11 and make any needed corrections.

ELECTRICAL READINGS FOR A CIRCUIT

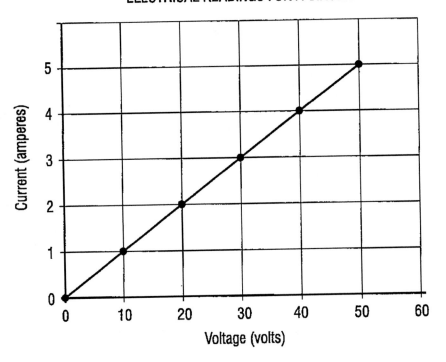

Figure 11
Electrical readings for a circuit

Ask your teacher to explain anything you don't understand about drawing a line graph. When you have cleared up any questions, try the next activity.

Study Activity: Traveling at 50 miles per hour, you record the mileage on your odometer every 30 minutes, as shown below.

Time (min)	Distance traveled (mi)
0	0
30	25
60	50
90	75
120	100

Draw and label the axes for your graph. Use the labels and title in the table above to help you label the axes. Put the driving time along the bottom line, 0, 30, 60, 90, and 120, and distances traveled along the line at the left, up to 100. Then plot the information from the table, using the driving time and the distance traveled.

Plot each set of data given in the table, and then join the points on the graph with lines.

Your graph should be a straight line. If your graph is not fairly straight, check your points and plot them again. According to your graph, on your next trip (at the same speed) about how many miles can you travel in 50 minutes? How many in 100 minutes? Remember that you are interpolating with your graph, and the result is only an estimate.

Suppose you wanted to show the bottom axis in hours, rather than minutes. Relabel your bottom axis in hours, without replotting your points.

Can you now use your graph to tell how far you could travel in 3 hours? Do you think this is a reasonable **extrapolation** of your graph?

SUMMARY

Reading graphs

You have learned to read and construct graphs and tables as you studied this chapter. As you read or get information from a graph, it is important that you know the kind of information you are getting. The labels and titles help you get general information and the units help you get specific information about the data in the graph.

Graphs show patterns, trends, differences, and other comparisons. Graphs can be a snapshot of conditions at one time, as in circle graphs, or they can show trends and patterns over time, as in bar graphs and line graphs.

You may have to estimate values on graphs when they fall between two labeled lines. If the point on the graph is about halfway, take the difference between the labeled lines, multiply by ½, and add this result to the lower value.

When you read line and bar graphs, remember that each point has two values—one from the horizontal axis and one from the vertical axis. It is a good procedure to start at the origin (your reference point), "go to the right," read the horizontal value, "then go up" and read the vertical value.

Constructing graphs

You need to make several decisions to construct graphs. You must decide on the *kind of graph* to use, the *choice of units* that fit the space you have, and how to *label the axes*.

If you are displaying current conditions or comparing parts to a whole, the circle graph has a good visual impact and may be your best choice.

Bar graphs give good visual impact and can show trends. Many people choose bar graphs when there are just a few quantities to be compared.

Line graphs are very helpful when you want to display a large amount of related data, to show trends, and to provide the opportunity for extensions of the data.

Some hints for drawing graphs include the following suggestions:

- Determine the range of data to be displayed (difference between the largest and smallest quantity in the data).

- Determine the units to use for each axis and the scale so all the data can be displayed. If one of the units is time, it is usually shown on the horizontal axis.

- Plot the data and draw the bars, or join the points with a line. On a circle graph, draw pie sections.

- Examine the completed graph to help you decide if the data are displayed so that comparisons and trends are shown.

PRACTICING THE SKILLS

Laboratory Activity

Use the mathematics skills you have learned to complete the following activity.

Activity:	**Measuring relative humidity**
Equipment	Sling psychrometer Wet-bulb/dry-bulb—relative humidity table

Statement of problem

The humidity in the air, often reported as relative humidity, can affect manufacturing processes. For instance, high humidity can affect the quality of polymers in tires and plastics and the quality of a paint job. The goal in most manufacturing plants is to keep the humidity low.

In this lab, you will measure relative humidity by using two thermometers in an arrangement called a sling psychrometer. One thermometer has a wet wick on the bulb and gives the wet-bulb temperature reading. The other thermometer has a dry-bulb and gives the dry-bulb temperature reading. The difference in the two readings is related to the relative humidity. The relative humidity is the value in the table your teacher gave you that corresponds to the dry-bulb column and the wet-bulb row.

Procedure

a. Obtain the equipment listed above from your teacher.

b. Moisten the wick material on the wet-bulb by dipping it into water near room temperature.

c. Grasp the handle of the psychrometer firmly and whirl the thermometers around for about 1 minute.

d. After one minute read the temperature on the wet-bulb thermometer. Record this value in the data table as wet-bulb temperature 1 for the classroom.

e. Repeat Steps **c** and **d** until consecutive readings do not change.

f. Repeat Steps **b** through **e** for a location chosen by your instructor that is outside the building.

g. Repeat Steps **b** through **e** for a location—chosen by your teacher—that is not heated or air conditioned.

Data Table

Location	Dry-bulb temperature	First wet-bulb temperature	Second wet-bulb temperature	Third wet-bulb temperature	Relative humidity
Classroom					
Outside					
Inside					

Calculations

a. On the wet-bulb/dry-bulb—relative humidity table supplied by your teacher, read across to the dry-bulb temperature for the classroom.

b. Move down the column in the table for the dry-bulb temperature until you reach the wet-bulb temperature. This value is the relative humidity. Record the relative humidity in the data table. Remember to interpolate when temperature measurements do not equal those in the table.

c. Repeat Steps **a** and **b** for the two remaining locations.

Discussion

Is the relative humidity the same for all three locations? If it is not, discuss with the rest of the class the reason for the differences. Which location would be best suited for most manufacturing processes?

STUDENT EXERCISES

You can solve the exercises that follow by applying the mathematics skills you've learned. The problems described here are those you may meet in the world of work.

EXERCISE 1: Information about the total highway mileage traveled by vehicles in the United States is shown in the graph below.

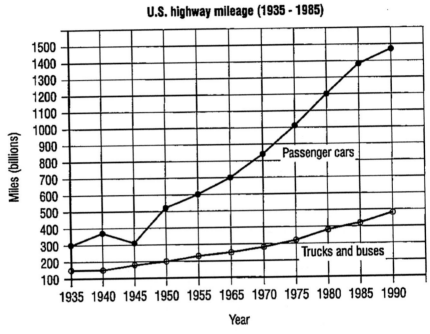

U.S. highway mileage (1935 - 1985)

a. What types of vehicles are referred to by this graph?

b. What span of time is covered by the graph?

c. The total mileage traveled each year is increasing. Which type of vehicle is increasing its total mileage faster?

d. Use the graph to estimate how many miles trucks and buses will travel in the year 1990. Do you think this would be a reliable estimate?

EXERCISE 2: An industrial plant suspects that the moisture in the air (the humidity) aggravates the production process, creating more factory rejects. To examine this suspicion, you are asked to compare the past year's reject levels with area weather data, shown below.

Month	Reject level (%)	Average absolute humidity (%)	Month	Reject level (%)	Average absolute humidity (%)
Jan	5.3	1.5	Jul	5.4	1.7
Feb	5.5	1.8	Aug	4.5	1.5
Mar	4.8	1.6	Sep	5.7	1.9
Apr	10.0	2.6	Oct	8.5	2.5
May	9.9	2.9	Nov	6.9	2.1
Jun	6.2	2.0	Dec	5.7	1.8

a. Plot the data, using the humidity as the horizontal axis and the reject level as the vertical axis. Determine the range of values needed to plot all the values shown in the table.

b. Does there seem to be a trend in the data, as shown by the plot?

c. Draw a long, single line with your ruler that passes through or very near most of the plotted points. Is it easy enough to do to make you think that there may be a relationship between the moisture and the reject level?

d. As the humidity gets higher, does the reject level appear to increase or decrease?

EXERCISE 3: The bar graph below shows the average braking distance required for a medium-sized car traveling at different speeds on dry pavement. The braking distance is measured from the time the brakes are applied until the car comes to a complete stop.

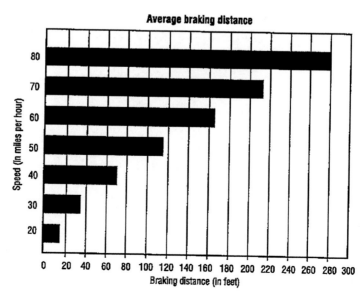

Average braking distance

Chapter 7: Using Graphs, Charts, and Tables

a. What is the unit of measurement used to indicate the braking distance?

b. What is the braking distance shown for a car traveling at a speed of 50 miles per hour (mph)?

c. Does it take about twice as far to stop a car that's going twice as fast?

EXERCISE 4: The circle graph below shows a general breakdown of how the average person uses time.

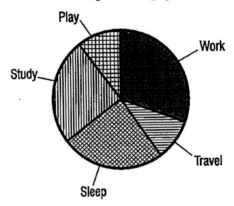

Activities during an average person's life

a. What is the most time-consuming activity for the average person?

b. About what fraction (or percent) of a person's life is spent sleeping?

c. Using the same categories as in the graph, redraw the graph to reflect your life.

EXERCISE 5: Pictured below is a graph of precipitation (rain, snow, and so on) for a certain region. This type of graph has the feature of indicating ranges of values, and is useful when construction projects are being planned in the region.

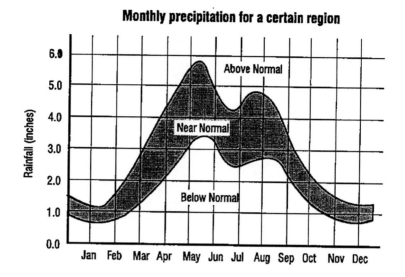

Monthly precipitation for a certain region

a. The graph indicates three ranges of precipitation—what are they?

b. What unit of measurement is used for the amount of rainfall?

c. What amounts of rainfall would be considered normal for August in this region (give the largest and the smallest amounts)?

d. What month(s) appear to be the driest (have the least precipitation)?

EXERCISE 6: Below is a table showing the change in social security employee rate for the past several years.

Social security tax rate for employees' withholding

Year	FICA rate
1970	4.80%
1971	5.20%
1972	5.20%
1973	5.85%
1974	5.85%
1975	5.85%
1976	5.85%
1977	5.85%
1978	6.05%
1979	6.13%
1980	6.13%
1981	6.65%
1982	6.70%
1983	6.70%
1984	6.70%
1985	7.05%
1986	7.15%
1987	7.15%
1988	7.51%

a. Construct a line graph of the FICA rate by year. Label years along one axis and the percentage rate along the other axis.

b. Examine the graph. Is the trend a steady increase, or does it appear to follow some kind of pattern?

c. Based on the brief study of the trends done above, how reliable might an estimate of the future FICA rate be (based on the graph)?

d. You should have the data points for 1984 and 1985 connected with a sloping line. Does this mean that the FICA rate was gradually changing between these two points?

EXERCISE 7: A large company produces a certain machine part. The company can produce the part either by casting or by forging. The tooling cost for casting is quite expensive, but the labor and material cost is relatively low compared to the forging method. With the forging method, the tooling cost is lower but the labor and material cost is higher. A graph of these relationships is shown below.

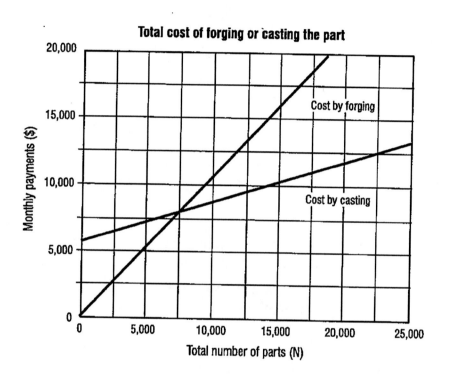

Total cost of forging or casting the part

a. For an order for 15,000 parts, what is the cost of producing the part by casting? By forging?

b. For an order for 5000 parts, what is the cost of producing the part by casting? By forging?

c. At what size order are the cost of forging and the cost of casting the same?

d. Can the "breakpoint" determined above be used as a guideline for the production staff? What would that guideline be?

EXERCISE 8:   As men and women age, the amount of energy used by the body when at rest, called the basal metabolic rate, decreases. The graph below shows the normal rates.

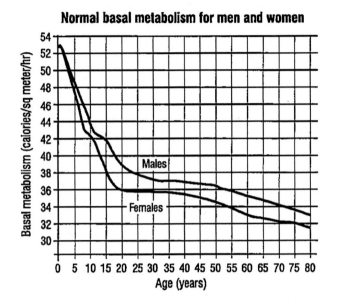

Normal basal metabolism for men and women

a. What is the unit of measurement for the basal metabolic rate shown in the graph?

b. How are the values for men and women distinguished in the graph?

c. A lab result indicates that a ten-year-old male patient has a rate of 70 calories/m²/hr. A rate of twice normal is considered hyperactivity. Would this patient be considered hyperactive?

EXERCISE 9: The Morgans have been renting an apartment for several years and are considering buying a house. A real estate agent provides them with the table shown below. It shows the monthly loan payments for various loan amounts and terms. (**Note:** The loan payments listed do not include taxes, insurance, and so on.)

Monthly payments needed to finance a loan

Amount of loan	10% Time of loan		12% Time of loan		14% Time of loan	
	20 yr	30 yr	20 yr	30 yr	20 yr	30 yr
$50,000	$482.52	$428.79	$550.55	$514.31	$621.77	$592.44
60,000	579.02	526.55	660.66	617.17	746.12	710.93
70,000	675.52	614.31	770.77	720.03	870.47	829.42
80,000	772.02	702.06	880.87	822.90	994.82	947.90
90,000	868.52	789.82	990.98	925.76	1119.17	1066.39
100,000	965.03	877.58	1101.09	1028.62	1243.53	1184.88
110,000	1061.53	965.33	1211.20	1131.48	1367.88	1303.37
120,000	1158.03	1053.09	1321.31	1234.34	1492.23	1421.85
130,000	1254.53	1140.85	1431.42	1337.20	1616.58	1540.34
140,000	1351.04	1228.61	1541.53	1440.06	1740.93	1658.83
150,000	1447.54	1316.36	1651.63	1542.92	1865.29	1777.31

a. What percent interest rates are covered in the table?

b. The Morgans want a 30-year loan, available now at 10% annual interest. Make a line graph of the monthly loan payments needed for each loan amount. Use the amount of the loan on one axis and the monthly payment on the other axis.

c. Using the graph, estimate how much the monthly loan payment would be for a loan amount of $85,500.

d. Can the graph be used to estimate the monthly payment for a $180,000 loan amount? If so, what do you think it would be?

EXERCISE 10: How can you budget for the cost of electricity for home heating and cooling? You may consider examining your monthly usage patterns. Below is a graph of the monthly electric usage for the past year.

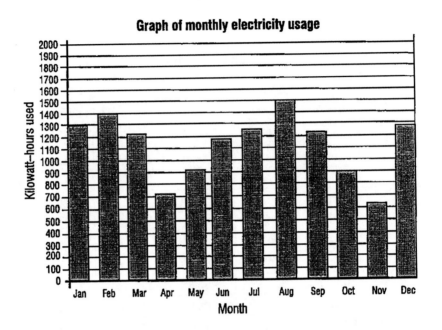

Graph of monthly electricity usage

a. What is the unit of measure for the electricity usage?

b. What is the highest amount of electricity usage shown on the graph?

c. When does the highest usage occur?

d. Are there several months of high usage, or just one month?

EXERCISE 11: The table below shows guidelines for allowable spans for 2 by 8, 2 by 10, and 2 by 12 floor joists of various types of wood. The allowable spans are given for 16" on center (OC) and 24" on center constructions.

Floor joists: maximum allowable spans

Species or species group	Grade	2 by 8		2 by 10		2 by 12	
		16" OC	24" OC	16" OC	24" OC	16" OC	24" OC
Douglas fir/arch	2 & better	13' 1"	11' 3"	16' 9"	14' 5"	20' 4"	17' 6"
	3	10' 7"	8' 8"	13' 6"	11' 0"	16' 5"	13' 5"
Hem/fir	2 & better	12' 3"	10' 0"	15' 8"	12' 10"	19' 1"	15' 7"
	3	9' 5"	7' 8"	12' 0"	9' 10"	14' 7"	11' 11"
Mountain hemlock	2 & better	11' 4"	9' 11"	14' 6"	12' 8"	17' 7"	15' 4"
	3	9' 7"	7' 10"	12' 3"	10' 0"	14' 11"	12' 2"
Western hemlock	2 & better	12' 3"	10' 6"	15' 8"	13' 4"	19' 1"	16' 3"
	3	9' 11"	8' 1"	12' 8"	10' 4"	15' 5"	12' 7"
Engelmann spruce	2 & better	11' 2"	9' 1"	14' 3"	11' 7"	17' 3"	14' 2"
	3	8' 6"	6' 11"	10' 10"	8' 10"	13' 2"	10' 9"
Lodgepole pine	2 & better	11' 8"	9' 7"	14' 11"	12' 3"	18' 1"	14' 11"
	3	9' 1"	7' 5"	11' 7"	9' 5"	14' 1"	11' 6"
Ponderosa pine & sugar pine	2 & better	11' 4"	9' 3"	14' 5"	11' 9"	17' 7"	14' 4"
	3	8' 8"	7' 1"	11' 1"	9' 1"	13' 6"	11' 0"
Idaho white pine	2 & better	11' 0"	9' 0"	14' 0"	11' 6"	17' 1"	14' 0"
	3	8' 6"	6' 11"	10' 10"	8' 10"	8' 10"	10' 9"
Western cedars	2 & better	11' 0"	9' 7"	14' 0"	12' 3"	17' 0"	14' 11"
	3	9' 1"	7' 5"	11' 6"	9' 5"	14' 0"	11' 6"

Design criteria: 10 pounds per square foot "dead" load plus 40 pounds per square foot "live" load.

Span (feet and inches)

a. You are using grade-2, 2-by-10 Douglas fir floor joists, spaced 16" OC. What does the table suggest as the maximum allowable span?

b. Could you span a farther distance by selecting a different type wood (species)? If so, what type?

c. If all you had available was grade-2 Engelmann spruce to be spaced 16" OC, which size(s) of lumber could you select for a floor span of 12 feet?

EXERCISE 12: The chart below shows the recommended amount of insulation for various parts of the United States, based on the climate zones. Amounts of insulation are measured by the resistance to heat flow. Insulation materials are rated by "R-values"—the higher the R-value of a material, the better it will insulate. Examine the chart below, both the map and the insert, and answer the questions.

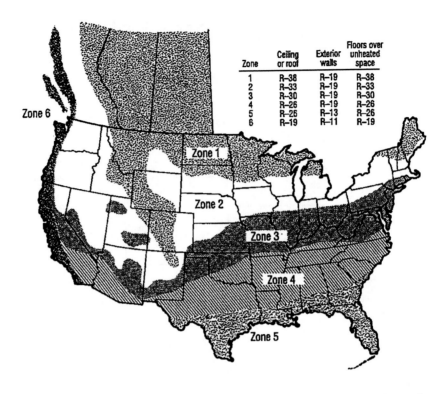

Zone	Ceiling or roof	Exterior walls	Floors over unheated space
1	R–38	R–19	R–38
2	R–33	R–19	R–33
3	R–30	R–19	R–30
4	R–26	R–19	R–26
5	R–26	R–13	R–26
6	R–19	R–11	R–19

a. How many different climate zones are indicated on the chart?

b. Examine the ceiling insulation recommendations. Is more ceiling insulation needed in the cold northern climates (zones 1 and 2), or the warmer southern climates?

c. If you lived in Florida (Zone 5), what R-value would be recommended for your home's exterior walls?

EXERCISE 13: You work as a quality control supervisor at a glass factory. A technician prepares a report on the rejected bottles with a graph, as shown below.

a. What range of dates does the defect report cover? How many days of production data are shown?

b. What is the highest level of defects reported on the graph?

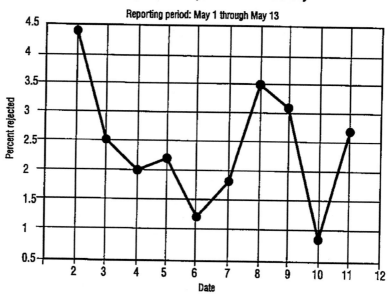

Biweekly defect report—Glass factory

Reporting period: May 1 through May 13

c. What is the lowest level of defects reported on the graph?

d. On what day did the highest level of defects occur?

EXERCISE 14: Automobile engines develop torque, the twisting power used to turn the car's wheels. A plot of engine torque is shown below.

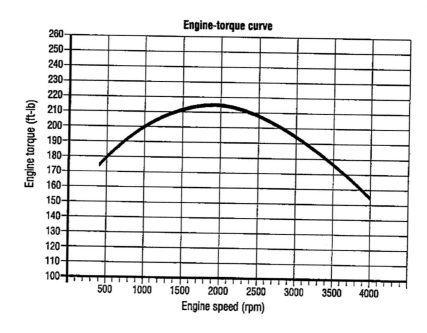

Engine-torque curve

a. Describe what happens to the torque as the engine speed is increased up to 4000 revolutions per minute. Does it get less and less? Or more and more? Or reach a maximum then drop off? Or reach a minimum then increase again?

b. What measure of engine speed does the graph use?

c. At about what engine speed does the graph indicate that the highest torque is developed?

EXERCISE 15: As a lab technician, you must perform various tests of material properties. Performing a stress analysis on wire samples is one such test. Shown below are the results of a stress analysis on a length of copper wire. The stretch of the wire is measured as different weights are hung from the wire.

Stress analysis on copper wire

Load (lb)	Stretch (inches)
0	0.00
2	0.02
4	0.04
6	0.06
8	0.08
10	0.10
12	0.13
14	0.64

a. Construct a graph of the stretch in the copper wire at each load. Label the load along one axis and the stretch along the other axis.

b. Interpret the graph to estimate the load limit for this wire. Show the load at which the wire will stretch to the point of breaking.

c. Can you estimate what the stretch might be at 3 pounds? If so, what is your estimate?

EXERCISE 16: For relatively low altitudes, air temperature decreases as the altitude increases, a fact with which early aviators had to cope. A graph of some typical measurements appears below.

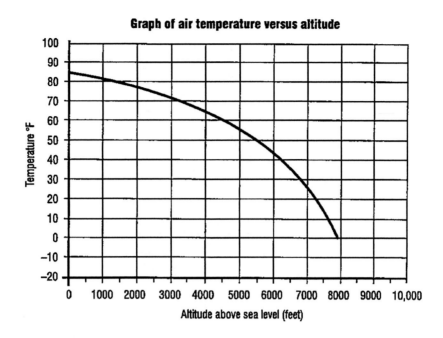

Graph of air temperature versus altitude

a. What are the units of measurement for altitude and for temperature in the graph?

b. How much has the temperature decreased from sea level to an altitude of 3000 feet?

c. Think about extending the line to estimate the temperature at 10,000 feet and at 15,000 feet. How reliable do you think these estimates are?

EXERCISE 17: Thermocouples are used to measure temperature. A thermocouple generates a voltage when heated. Using calibration curves and tables, the measured voltage can be converted to a temperature reading. Types of thermocouples are identified by a letter, such as type E, type K, and so on. Calibration curves for comparison of different types of thermocouples are shown below.

a. What temperature scale does the graph use to display the thermocouple comparisons?

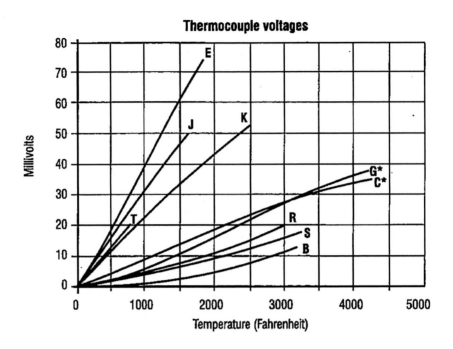

Thermocouple voltages

b. What are the different types of thermocouples shown in the graph?

c. What type will generate the most voltage at 1500°F?

EXERCISE 18: A test of twenty 30-amp fuses shows that not all the fuses are "breaking" at the rated amperage. The table of data is shown below.

Breaking point for sampled 30-A fuses

Breaking point range (amperes)	Number of fuses
24 – 25	1
26 – 27	3
28 – 29	5
30 – 31	8
32 – 33	2
34 – 35	1

a. Construct a bar graph of the data. Label the ranges of breaking points on one axis, and the number of fuses "breaking" in those ranges on the other axis.

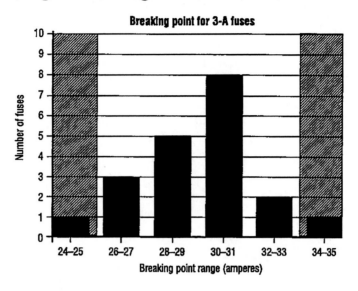

Breaking point for 3-A fuses

b. Is the most frequently occurring "breakpoint" near the rated amperage of the fuses? If not, where is it?

c. On your graph, shade in the test results that indicate "breakpoints" outside a tolerance range of 26 amps to 33 amps. See the shaded areas on the graph in Part **a.**

EXERCISE 19: The graph below shows both the indoor and outdoor temperatures for a 12-hour period.

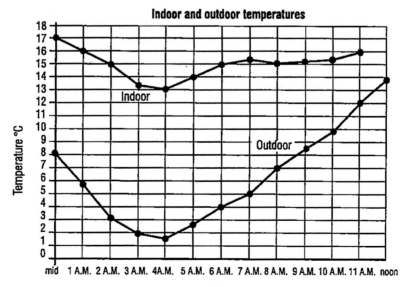

Indoor and outdoor temperatures

a. What are the units used to indicate the temperatures?

b. What 12-hour period is depicted?

c. Do the indoor and outdoor temperatures seem to be related?

d. When is the greatest difference in temperature observed? What is the temperature difference at this time?

EXERCISE 20: You are making a presentation to a citizens' group about the cost of television sets marketed by your firm. Below is a circle graph showing the breakdown of cost for a particular television set.

Distribution of cost of televisions

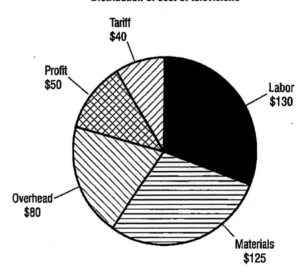

a. What portion ($) of the total cost goes to cover the cost of labor and materials?

b. What would be the total cost of the television if no tariff were imposed on imported parts?

c. Estimate what percent of the total cost is profit to the company.

Chapter 8

Dealing with Data

How to collect, organize, and interpret data
to solve problems

Prerequisites   This chapter builds on the skills taught in

Chapter 4: *Learning Problem-Solving Techniques*
Chapter 6: *Measuring in English and Metric Units*
Chapter 7: *Using Graphs, Charts, and Tables*

**To Master
This Chapter**   Read the text and answer all the questions. Complete the assigned exercises and activity. Work the problems on the chapter test at a satisfactory level.

**Chapter
Objectives**   Working through this chapter helps you learn how to:

1. Recognize a problem that needs more data, and find a source for those data.

2. Collect the data you need to solve a problem.

3. Organize the data to help you solve the problem.

4. Interpret or use the data so you can solve the problem.

LEARNING THE SKILLS

INTRODUCTION

You're on your way to work and you tune in the local radio station. The disc jockey is announcing the latest results of a political poll. Later that day you begin to wonder how the poll was determined. Who determined the results? How could the pollsters be sure their results were correct?

How does a polling agency determine the ranking of political candidates? They must contact many people and collect lots of information or facts. These facts are called data. Finally, after studying these data, they are able to decide and tell us the ranking of the candidates.

Just like the polling agency, you have to make decisions and solve problems. Good decisions are easier to make if you first locate and gather the facts you need. This chapter helps you:

- recognize problems for which you need more information before you can solve them.
- learn where to find the information you need.
- collect the data you need.
- organize the data so you can work with them.
- interpret the data so you can solve a problem, or make a decision.

What exactly are data?

Data are *facts*—or factual information. Facts often are expressed as numbers. Such numbers are found in lists—as in telephone directories and sales catalogs. You may find facts on the labels of products you buy. You also can find them in tables—often referred to as "statistics." No matter where we find them, data are useful information that is needed to help solve problems.

Who uses data?

Many people read and interpret data as part of their daily work.

- Contractors read the data printed on labels for paints and sealers.

- Auto mechanics, people who repair small engines, and people who work with radios, televisions, or computers find data in instruction and maintenance manuals.

- Health-care workers read and interpret the data for medicines given to patients.

- Dietitians develop a suitable diet after collecting and interpreting the data about the patient.

All of these workers use the data they find to solve problems on their jobs.

Where can you find data?

Sometimes you meet a problem and discover that you do not have enough data—or information—to solve the problem.

Before you start working the problem, stop for a minute and think— "Do I have all the data I need to solve this?"

If you need more data, ask yourself, "Where can I find the data?" Sometimes you can find data by asking an expert. More often, however, you get data from records, tables, measurements, or observations.

Figure 1
Gathering data from many sources

You can find data in many places. Here is a list of sources where data can be found:

- Experts
- News broadcasts
- Newspapers
- Magazines
- Trade journals
- Computer data banks

- Catalogs
- Textbooks
- Encyclopedias
- Library references
- Shop manuals
- Owner operator manuals

In this chapter you will learn how to collect data and facts yourself. When you obtain data for yourself, you can be sure they relate to your problem.

SOLVING A PROBLEM DEALING WITH DATA

Let's try to understand how "dealing with data" can help us solve actual problems. Think about the following problem. It is a very real problem for families trying to control a grocery budget.

Choosing the store with the lowest prices

A young couple is trying to control their grocery budget. There are seven grocery stores in their city where they can shop. Only four are near their home, though. They would like to shop at the one store that has the lowest prices. The young couple realizes they need some more information before they can choose the "best" store.

How would you suggest the young couple go about selecting a store? Write down on a piece of paper some ways they could choose the store with the lowest prices. The young couple's ideas are in the next section. Compare your ways with theirs.

Getting the data

In general, when you set out to solve a problem that needs data, you will go through three steps to collect the data.

1. Decide whether you need more data.
2. Find a source for the data.
3. Collect the data.

Sometimes you can stop after the first step. You can solve your problem without collecting more information. At other times, you will see that you need more data and need to go through all three steps.

Let's see how the young couple gets the data they need.

The young couple knows they need more data. They decide that they need to *collect* some grocery prices from each of the stores. There are many ways they can get these prices. Here are some ways they thought of:

- Grocery receipts from the past several weeks
- Telephone calls to each store about prices
- Sales inserts in the local newspapers
- Price tags on items at the store

Are any of these methods better than the others? Can you think of other ways they might collect the data they need?

As you can see, there is more than one way to collect the data. But the *way* you collect the data can be important, too. What makes one way to collect data better than other ways? Think about these three points.

Accuracy of data you collect—if you need accurate results, choose the way to collect data that produces the most reliable numbers or facts. Sometimes this will mean much work to collect the data. For example, a polling agency got data from several people through phone surveys. Asking only one store would have produced an unreliable ranking.

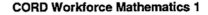

Time needed to collect data—if you are in a hurry, collect data in the fastest possible way. Often, however, this may result in less accuracy. For example, paramedics do not have time to perform a complete physical exam on an accident victim. Collecting the "vital signs" is usually sufficient to provide the proper care.

Trouble and expense involved in collecting data—which way is easiest and involves the least effort or travel on your part? On your job, this often will be a major concern. For example, you probably would not want to spend $100 collecting data to solve a problem that is costing you $50.

Which way did the young couple decide to get their data? They chose to look through the last several weeks of newspapers in their house. They planned to collect price data from the ads for each store. Do you think this was the best method? The quickest? The easiest?

Figure 2
Accuracy, time, and expense are important.

The couple found that there were a lot of data in the newspaper ads. So, instead of dealing with *all* the data in the ads, they decided to choose a few common items. They got the prices for milk, bread, ground beef, tuna, tomato sauce, coffee, dog food, and laundry soap. They also decided to collect data from only four nearby stores: ABC Grocery, Saveway, Grocery Mart, and XYZ Foods.

Figure 3
Collecting the data

The young couple collected the price data from the
newspaper ads. This way, they could try to find the store
with the lowest prices. Suppose you had to find the lowest
prices on several items you needed. How would *you* find the
best store?

Let's review some of the decisions the young couple made to
solve their problem.

1. They decided to check the prices at only four nearby
   stores. This made the job of collecting data much easier
   and quicker.

2. They decided to collect prices on only a few common
   items. This also made the collecting job much easier.
   They also were looking ahead to the job of choosing the
   best store. With fewer items to compare, the job of
   picking the best store should be easier.

3. They decided to use the newspaper ads as their source of
   prices. They chose this way mainly because it was quick
   and easy. The other ways may be more accurate, but not
   as easy.

ORGANIZING YOUR DATA

The young couple is trying to control their grocery expenses. You have seen how they collected prices from four grocery stores. Now they need to *organize* the data so they can decide which store to use.

Sometimes when you collect data to solve a problem you have a lot of information. To determine rankings, a polling agency called hundreds of people. The polling staff must have a good way to organize all these data to determine the most popular hits.

Like the polling agency, the young couple has collected lots of data. They now must organize their grocery prices. They do this so they can make the right decision about where to buy their groceries.

Here are some of the most common ways to organize data:
- Making a tally or count
- Making a graph
- Drawing a picture
- Making a table or a list

You can use a *tally* to organize your data when you are counting items. You probably have seen tally sheets with lots of "tic" marks. These "tic" marks help you to organize your data while you are collecting them. Polls usually are collected and organized by a tally. A tally, as shown in Figure 4, keeps the count for each choice as you collect the data.

Figure 4
Organizing data by tallying

Drawing a *graph* can be very helpful in organizing data values that are changing. You may have seen graphs of the stock market performance as shown in Figure 5, or the trace of the electrical data from a person's heartbeat. As you can imagine, it is much easier to understand a "picture" of the data than a page full of numbers.

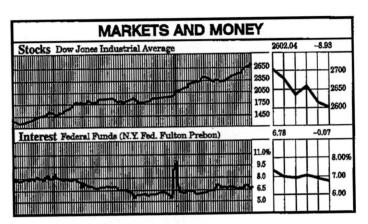

Figure 5
Organizing data by graphing

Pictures are also a very helpful way to organize measurements. For example, you can record measurements for a house on a sketch of a house floor plan. This is easier than trying to describe which wall is 12 feet long, where the door lies, and so on. Dental technicians record cavities and fillings for a patient on a drawing of the patient's upper and lower teeth, as shown in Figure 6.

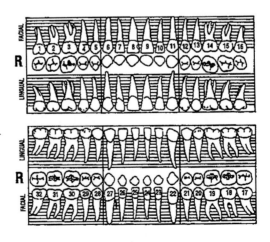

Figure 6
Organizing data with a picture

If you group your data together in columns or rows, you can organize them in a *table* or a *list*. The data in each column—and each row—will have a feature in common. (You'll see this later, in Figure 8.) You frequently will see data organized like this in reference manuals and sheets. Pricing lists of all sorts usually are shown in tables or lists. You will see recipes listed: the quantity of each ingredient and the ingredient's name. We normally see payroll data for each day's work organized in a table. Payroll clerks will record the hours worked each day of the week for each employee in columns and rows. Tables of data are very common, as shown in Figure 7.

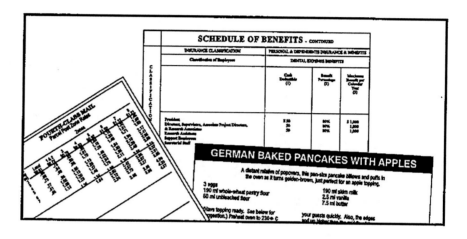

Figure 7
Organizing data with tables

How did the young couple choose to organize their data?

They looked at their data: the newspaper ads with circled prices. They had prices for several stores and several common items from each store. They saw that they could organize their data in a table, as shown in Figure 8 below. All the prices shown under the first column are from ABC Grocery, under the second column are from Saveway Store, and so on. Similarly, all the prices shown in the first row are for milk, prices in the second row are for bread, and so on.

	ABC GROCERY	SAVEWAY STORE	GROCERY MART	XYZ FOODS
MILK	2.49	2.79	2.25	2.56
BREAD	1.01	.92	.97	.97
GROUND BEEF	1.88	1.95	1.90	1.79
TUNA	.89	.79	.76	.93
TOMATO SAUCE	.24	.25	.20	.24
COFFEE	2.99	3.49	2.89	3.15
DOG FOOD	4.99	5.49	5.19	5.87
LAUNDRY SOAP	2.78	3.05	3.05	2.96

Figure 8
Organizing the grocery prices

The young couple chose a table because they could see their price data easily and analyze them in that form. The method you select to organize your data will depend on what kind of data you've collected, and how you plan to interpret them. You may choose to tally your data, show them in a graph or picture, or make a list or table with them.

INTERPRETING YOUR DATA

Let's review.

When you meet a problem that needs more information to be solved, you need to collect data. You must consider where to find the data and how to collect them. You then need to organize the data so you can understand them and solve your problem. "Making sense" out of organized data is what we call *interpreting* the data.

You can interpret data in basically three ways.

Comparing different parts of the organized data to determine the best price, the highest quality, the most quantity, and so on. For example, the young couple can compare the bread prices to find which store has the lowest price.

Calculating totals, averages, differences, and so forth for different parts of the data. For example, the young couple may use their receipts from the past several weeks to calculate the total spent on groceries each month.

Predicting trends or patterns indicated by the data. For example, the young couple can look at their monthly grocery expenses and see if they are increasing, decreasing, or staying about the same.

The young couple's problem was to select the grocery store with the lowest prices. First, they collected some prices for common items from several stores. Then they organized the different prices (their data) in a table. At this point they were ready to examine the data and try to solve their problem. How would *you* proceed to find the best store for the young couple? On your paper, write down ways you would use to pick the best store.

Remember that in the young couple's problem, they were looking for the lowest prices. Therefore, *comparing* prices from the different stores is a good way to interpret their data. When comparing data to make a decision, you usually will look for the biggest or smallest, the best or worst, the fastest or slowest, and so on. This is why organizing your data is important. If you can organize your data so it is easy to compare different items in the data, interpreting the data should be fairly easy.

The young couple arranged their data in a table, with prices listed under each store name (see Figure 8). They decided to *compare* each store's prices and circle the *lowest* price for each item, as shown in Figure 9. Is "comparing" one of the ways you wrote down?

Look at the circled items. On your paper, write the name of the store you think has the lowest price.

After considering the circled prices, the young couple *thought* about another way to interpret their data. They decided to calculate the total of the prices for each store, *and* compare the totals. You can try the same thing now, using your calculator. Find the totals for each store yourself, and look for the lowest total. Is the choice of store different from the choice made by comparing item prices?

	ABC GROCERY	SAVEWAY STORE	GROCERY MART	XYZ FOODS
MILK	2.49	2.79	(2.25)	2.56
BREAD	1.01	(.92)	.97	.97
GROUND BEEF	1.88	1.95	1.90	(1.79)
TUNA	.89	.79	(.76)	.93
TOMATO SAUCE	.24	.25	(.20)	.24
COFFEE	2.99	3.49	(2.89)	3.15
DOG FOOD	(4.99)	5.49	5.19	5.87
LAUNDRY SOAP	(2.78)	3.05	3.05	2.96

Figure 9
Circling the lowest prices

There is one final way the young couple might want to interpret their data. You may have thought of it already. When the young couple selects a store, they hope it will continue to have the lowest prices. This way of thinking involves *predicting*.

When they predict the future with data, they must be careful. The young couple must consider whether the store prices seem to be staying the same. An interpretation like this may need more data. For example, if they had collected their data for each month of the past year, they could examine the trend of the prices. They might find that one store *always* had the lowest prices. They could safely predict that this trend might continue in the coming year.

The young couple did not collect their data over a year's time. However, they felt the prices for these stores were staying pretty much the same. They felt confident that the Grocery Mart should be their choice. It had the lowest *total price*. They felt comparing the total prices was the best way to interpret their data. They also that it would be a good idea to watch the prices during the coming year for any big change.

Summary of the young couple's problem

Let's go back over the young couple's problem one last time.

Recall they were trying to control their grocery budget. To help do this, they felt they should select the grocery store that offered the lowest prices. They decided to compare prices from four nearby stores. Then they *collected* price data from a handy source: newspaper ads.

The young couple *organized* the data in a table. They listed the names of the four stores across the top. They listed the common food items in a column down the left side of the table. Then they put the price for each item in the correct location in the table.

The young couple then *interpreted* the data in the table. First, they picked the store that had the largest number of low prices. Based on this interpretation, they picked the Grocery Mart as the best store. Then they decided that another way to choose the store with the lowest prices would be to calculate the overall total. This way still showed that the Grocery Mart had the lowest prices. The young couple good about interpreting their data this way.

The young couple also worried about whether the Grocery Mart would have the lowest prices during the coming year. They decided to keep track of the prices during the year and check their prediction.

The young couple is happy with their work. However, in checking over their data, they find a possible weakness in their interpretation. They buy coffee and laundry soap only once a month, but they buy milk, bread, and the other items every week. Do these additional data change the store they should select? Can you include these new data in the table, and interpret them? Should the young couple still shop at the Grocery Mart, as decided? Would another store be less expensive over a whole month?

OTHER PROBLEMS THAT DEAL WITH DATA

Now let's examine some other problems where data are needed to solve a problem.

Example 1:
Finding the best temperature

A landscaper grows plants for his business. Before he puts the plants out in the landscaping project, he sprouts the seeds in small pots in his greenhouse. If the sprouting temperature is too hot or too cold, the seeds don't grow well. The landscaper is trying to find the temperature that causes his seeds to sprout the best.

The landscaper uses his own observations and measurements to *collect* the data he needs. He does this as follows.

The landscaper plants 8 batches of seeds in separate boxes—6 plants per box. Each box has the same kind of soil and gets the same amount of water and light. He sets a different temperature for each box, and holds the temperature constant for seven days. After seven days, he measures the height of the sprouts in each box, and calculates the average height for each box. He records each box's average seedling height and temperature setting. His data appear in Figure 10, below.

Figure 10
Collecting data on seedling heights

The landscaper *organizes* his data by drawing a graph. He puts the control temperature (in degrees Fahrenheit) at the bottom. Along the side he puts the *average* seedling height (in inches). He uses the averages of his measurements to put an "×" on the graph for the average height at each of the different temperatures. Figure 11 shows his graph.

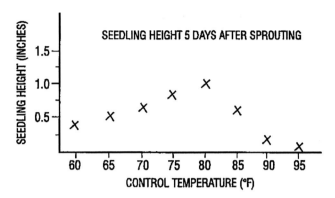

Figure 11
Graphing seedling height data

The landscaper is now ready to *interpret* his data to find the best temperature for sprouting his seedlings. Look at the data in the graph. On your own paper, write an approximate temperature that causes the seedlings to grow the highest. After you have written your answer, check it with the answer that follows.

The landscaper interprets his data by *comparing* the different average seedling heights shown by his data. His graph makes it very easy to see that the seedlings grew tallest at the temperature of 80°F. He *predicts* that in the future, his seeds should do about the same. He will watch them carefully to see that they continue to grow well at a temperature near 80°F.

Example 2:
Producing
conversion vans

A van-conversion company has been producing units while working at 80% of its production capacity. The manager of the company has the opportunity to provide vans to a new dealer. However, the new dealer will require the delivery of 10 conversions each week. The manager must decide if the company can produce the 10 additional units each week and still meet the current production needs.

The manager must *collect* data to help him make a decision. He decides to get the plant's weekly production totals for the past 6 weeks while it operated at 80% of its capacity. The numbers of units produced each week were as follows: Week 1: 52 units; Week 2: 51 units; Week 3: 53 units; Week 4: 53 units; Week 5: 51 units; Week 6: 52 units.

The manager can *organize* these data into a chart as shown in Figure 12.

Units Produced Per Week at 80% Capacity

Week	Units Produced
Week 1	52
Week 2	51
Week 3	53
Week 4	53
Week 5	51
Week 6	52
Average units per week	52

Figure 12
Weekly production of van conversions

The manager is now ready to *interpret* the data. He would like to know the average number of units produced each week by the company while operating at 80% capacity. Using a calculator, the manager *calculates* that the average is 52. He also uses the calculator to convert 100% and 80% to decimal numbers.

$$100\% = 1$$

$$80\% = 0.8$$

Next, the manager performs the following division.

$$\frac{1.0}{0.8} = 1.25$$

This calculation tells the manager that at 100% capacity the van-conversion rate will increase 1.25 times. With this information, he calculates 52×1.25 and determines that at 100% capacity the company can complete 65 conversions each week.

The manager can now determine if the 10 additional units per week would exceed the company's production capacity. He adds the current average weekly production of 52 units and the 10 new units per week required by the new dealer. The plant would need to produce 62 units each week.

The manager *compares* the 62 units needed each week with the company's capacity of producing 65 units each week. He *predicts* that, by increasing production to full capacity, the company will be able to provide the new dealer 10 units each week and still meet the current production needs.

SUMMARY

We call this chapter "Dealing with Data." That's because in some cases we can't solve a problem—or answer a question—without getting more data, or information. When that's necessary, we can use a logical method to gather and use the data to help solve our problem.

The first step is to *find a source* for the data that are needed. To find the grocery store with the lowest prices, the young couple thought about using grocery receipts, telephone calls to the stores, newspaper ads, and so on. They selected the newspaper ads because they were quick, easy, and fairly accurate. The landscaper decided to find the best temperature for sprouting seeds by measuring the seedlings himself. And we saw that the manager used company data to determine if the company was capable of producing enough converted vans.

The next step in solving a problem is to *collect the data*. The young couple collected their data from the newspaper ads for selected grocery items. The landscaper measured the heights of his seedlings under carefully controlled temperatures. The manager took information from the weekly production records of the company.

After collecting, you should *organize your data*. This makes them easier to understand and interpret. We saw how the young couple organized their grocery prices into a *table* of items and stores. The landscaper found that a *graph* of average seedling heights at each temperature made it very easy to see his data. The manager organized the data into a chart.

The final step is to *interpret your data* to solve your problem or answer your question. The young couple examined their table of prices and *computed* the totals for each store. They *compared* the totals for each store and selected the store with the lowest total price. By using his graph, the landscaper *compared* his seedling growths and was able to *predict* the best sprouting temperature for his seeds. The manager used the data to compute the average units produced each week. From this, he calculated what the company could produce at 100% capacity. This was compared to the production needs. The manager then predicted the company could meet the production needs.

All of us handle data in our personal lives and at work. The lab activity and exercises that follow provide you with some additional practice in collecting, organizing, and interpreting data to solve problems.

Here again are four steps for dealing with a problem that needs data:
1. Find a source for the data you need.
2. Collect the data.
3. Organize your data so you can understand them.
4. Interpret the data to solve the problem.

PRACTICING THE SKILLS

Laboratory Activity

Use the mathematics skills you have learned to complete the following activity.

Activity: Counting calories

Equipment Calorie counter
Food journal of all food eaten in the last three days
Calculator

Given Part of any plan to maintain or improve your health is a study of the diet. Such a study can begin with a review of the food eaten over a trial period. One area of importance is the number of calories consumed, especially if weight loss or gain is a concern.

Find 1. The recommended calorie intake for your age, weight, and height.

2. Whether your caloric intake is appropriate for you.

Procedure *Collect* 1. Determine a source for the recommended calorie intake.

2. Carry your journal with you for three days. For every meal and snack, record the type food and drink, and about how much of each you consume.

Organize 3. Organize your journal data into a table. Show the type of food and the quantity eaten. Be sure to record your food in appropriate units. For example, record liquids in fluid ounces, meats in pounds or ounces, bread by the slice, and so on.

4. Using the calorie counter, find each food item recorded in your journal. Add to your data table the number of calories per unit (ounce, cup, serving, and so on) for each food in your journal. Make sure your recorded units agree with the calorie counter's units.

5. Multiply the number of calories per unit by the amount you actually consumed. Place this number, the actual amount of calories eaten, in your data table.

Interpret   **6.** Determine the average calories you consumed during the three days.

7. Compare your average intake with the recommended intake.

STUDENT EXERCISES

You can solve the exercises that follow by applying the mathematics skills you've learned. The problems described here are those you may meet in the world of work.

EXERCISE 1: Two roommates are trying to reduce their total utility costs. They first want to know what their utilities are costing them now. Their monthly bills are paid to the electric company, the gas company, the water/sewer company, and the city garbage department. They have collected and organized the data shown below.

Month	Electric	Gas	Water/Sewer	Garbage
1	$ 92.89	$89.00	$28.47	$7.50
2	105.89	68.92	33.96	7.50
3	121.52	54.84	35.80	7.50
4	135.49	43.20	40.87	7.50
5	139.61	29.12	44.26	7.50
6	141.94	22.11	46.46	7.50
7	140.33	26.95	44.11	7.50
8	140.52	23.11	43.20	7.50
9	137.45	27.19	41.88	7.50
10	129.16	37.54	35.56	7.50
11	118.36	48.79	36.76	7.50
12	105.61	62.59	32.11	7.50

a. Find the average monthly utility cost for each type of utility. (The average monthly cost is the total cost per year divided by 12.)

b. Some electric utilities offer an "averaging plan." With this plan, your bill each month is the average of the previous 12 months (including the current month). If the roommates chose this plan, what would their electric bill require them to pay for the 12th month?

c. If their average electric bill is reduced by one third, how much can the roommates hope to save during a month? During a year?

EXERCISE 2: Ten apprenticeship trainees are competing for honors that are based on grade-point averages. The director of an apprenticeship training program is given their grade-point averages for each of the six sessions in the program. The director organizes them as shown below.

Session

Trainee	1	2	3	4	5	6
Paul A.	3.4	3.7	4.0	3.9	2.9	3.2
Robert C.	4.0	4.0	3.9	3.9	3.8	4.0
Walter F.	2.8	3.0	3.2	3.5	3.4	3.4
Scott G.	2.9	3.0	3.5	2.9	2.8	2.9
Cheryl H.	3.6	3.0	3.1	3.0	3.0	3.6
Evelyn K.	3.2	3.5	3.4	4.0	3.7	3.8
John L.	2.8	3.3	3.8	2.9	3.4	3.9
Agnes R.	3.7	3.9	3.9	3.8	3.9	4.0
Judy R.	2.6	2.4	3.0	2.5	2.8	2.6
Emma T.	3.7	3.2	3.0	3.2	3.6	3.5

a. Calculate the six-session average for each of the ten trainees. Organize the average data in a list.

b. Interpret the table to determine which trainee should receive the honor of the highest grade-point average. Which student should receive the honor of the second-highest grade-point average?

EXERCISE 3: Joshua is an electrician who has just received his first monthly paycheck at his new job, for the month of January. He wants to determine if his employer is withholding enough taxes. Examine the data below.

Paycheck stub for: Joshua Rogers
For the month of: January

GROSS WAGES	NET PAY
$1119.95	$872.15
SALARY INCOME	FED INCOME TAX
$1100.00	$118.80
COMMISSION	STATE INCOME TAX
$19.95	$46.50
	SOCIAL SECURITY
	$82.50

a. Interpret the data on this paycheck stub to determine Joshua's estimated annual gross wages, federal income tax, and state income tax for the current year.

b. Joshua has determined that he should owe about $1400 federal income tax at the end of the year. Is his employer withholding enough federal income tax each month?

c. In the electrician's home state, the annual state income tax is calculated to be $440 plus 8% of gross wages over $11,250. Interpret the annual wages to find the amount of state income tax due from Joshua at the end of the year. Is his employer withholding enough state tax each month?

EXERCISE 4: The coordinator of public tours for a soft drink bottling company serves complimentary soft drinks to the visitors when the plant tour has been completed. The coordinator normally orders small, medium, and large cups once a month, to keep a minimum inventory of 250 cups of each size. A review of her purchase orders for the last three months shows the following data.

> 1800 small, 1200 medium, 1900 large
>
> 1700 small, 1250 medium, 2150 large
>
> 1800 small, 1300 medium, 2200 large

The coordinator has noted that last week the plant served 628 small drinks, 265 medium drinks, and 481 large drinks to visitors. Is the coordinator likely to run out of drink cups during the next three weeks? (Assume that the orders are roughly the same as the monthly usages.)

EXERCISE 5: A company has a contract to replace the carpeting in a home. Presently, the floors are covered as follows:

- Living area, bedrooms, and closets are carpeted.
- Front entry is covered with ceramic tile.
- Kitchen and bath are covered with linoleum.

The company uses a solid brown carpet that is stocked in 12-foot-wide rolls. The carpet sells for $8.95 per square yard.

a. Study the floor plan drawn below. List the sizes of the rooms that will be carpeted.

b. Interpret the floor plan to determine how much carpet the company must purchase to recarpet the house. Run two widths across both bedrooms and 2 widths across the living room. Use 3 feet for the two closets.

c. Calculate the total cost of carpet needed.

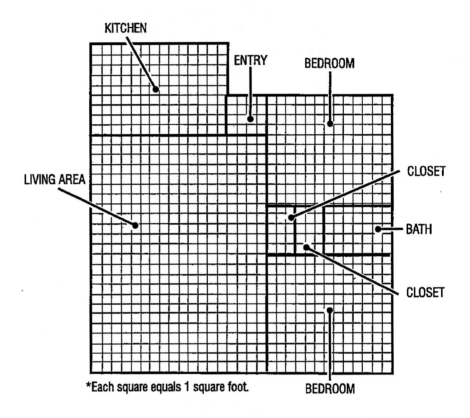

*Each square equals 1 square foot.

EXERCISE 6: A quality control inspector monitors a local weather station and records the daily maximum temperature to see what effect the temperature has on his company's product. The inspector collects this piece of data from the equipment each day, and posts it on a calendar. The inspector's calendar for this month is shown below.

Maximum daily temperature (°F)

Sun	Mon	Tue	Wed	Thu	Fri	Sat
	80	79	69	78	82	82
84	83	86	84	85	83	84
88	85	87	86	88	87	86
85	86	87	87	86	83	84
87	89	90				

a. The inspector has collected the data in a convenient calendar format. Organize the data using a simple graph that shows the temperature change over the span of the month. (Use the bottom axis for the day of the month, 1 through 30, and the side axis for the temperature, from 60°F to 100°F.)

b. Interpret the graph to determine days of the highest and lowest maximum temperatures for the month.

c. Find the average maximum temperature for the month. (Notice that neither the calendar format nor the graph is very helpful in calculating the average. Is there a better way to organize the data to do this?)

EXERCISE 7: An automotive parts store clerk is waiting on a customer who has a list. The clerk has identified the part numbers for his list, as shown below.

Customer's parts needed

Part no.	Quantity	Description
318439731	12	Spark plug set
847990617	23	Condenser
422540343	10	Distributor points
918705818	17	Carburetor kit
637423525	8	Needle valve
562251154	31	1" hose clamp
246522724	7	Ignition coil wire
853464136	13	Flywheel spring
247013296	2	Flywheel
943414322	12	Spark plug wire set

A quick look at the company's computer inventory screen reveals the partial parts list shown below.

Parts on hand

Part no.	Quantity	Description
101898762	9	Car polish
246522724	12	Ignition coil wire
247013296	1	Flywheel
318439731	32	Spark plug set
368472091	5	Metric wrench set
422540343	15	Distributor points
562251154	39	1" hose clamp
637423525	3	Needle valve
653981653	12	O-ring
762439408	75	Engine oil
847990617	23	Condenser
853464136	1	Flywheel spring
918705818	4	Carburetor kit
943414322	6	Spark plug wire set
976286119	34	Headlamp

Interpret the data to determine what parts (if any) need to be back ordered (that is, there is insufficient quantity to fill the order). How many of each should the clerk back order?

EXERCISE 8: A clerk in the shipping department of a glassware factory frequently must mail packages to customers. The clerk is required to figure the amount of postage, insurance, and other fees for these packages. The packages from the factory normally are sent as fourth-class mail. The clerk collects the data from charts supplied by the postal service, shown below.

FOURTH-CLASS MAIL
Parcel Post Zone Rates

Weight 1 pound and not exceeding (pounds)	Local	1 & 2	3	4	5	6	7	8
2	$0.61	$0.72	$0.75	$0.83	$.92	$1.02	$1.12	$1.21
3	.65	.78	.83	.92	1.04	1.18	1.32	1.45
4	.69	.84	.90	1.01	1.16	1.33	1.51	1.69
5	.73	.90	.98	1.10	1.28	1.49	1.71	1.93
6	.77	.96	1.05	1.19	1.40	1.64	1.90	2.17
7	.81	1.02	1.13	1.28	1.52	1.80	2.10	2.41
8	.85	1.08	1.20	1.37	1.64	1.95	2.29	2.65
9	.89	1.14	1.28	1.46	1.76	2.11	2.49	2.89
10	.93	1.20	1.35	1.55	1.88	2.26	2.68	3.13
11	.97	1.26	1.43	1.64	2.00	2.42	2.88	3.37
12	1.01	1.32	1.50	1.73	2.12	2.57	3.07	3.61
13	1.05	1.38	1.58	1.82	2.24	2.73	3.27	3.85
14	1.09	1.44	1.65	1.91	2.36	2.88	3.46	4.09
15	1.13	1.15	1.73	2.00	2.48	3.04	3.66	4.33
16	1.17	1.56	1.80	2.09	2.60	3.19	3.85	4.57
17	1.21	1.62	1.88	2.18	2.72	3.35	4.05	4.81
18	1.25	1.86	1.95	2.27	2.84	3.50	4.24	5.05
19	1.29	1.74	2.03	2.36	2.96	3.66	4.44	5.29
20	1.33	1.80	2.10	2.45	3.08	3.81	4.63	5.55
21	1.37	1.86	2.10	2.54	3.20	3.97	4.83	5.77
22	1.44	1.92	2.25	2.63	3.32	4.12	5.02	6.01
23	1.44	1.98	2.33	2.72	3.44	4.28	5.22	6.25
24	1.49	2.04	2.40	2.81	3.56	4.43	5.41	6.49
25	1.53	2.10	2.48	2.90	3.68	4.59	5.61	6.73

INSURANCE FEES

Value of Package	Fee
$.01 to $15.00	$0.20
15.01 to 50.00	0.30
50.01 to 100.00	0.40
100.01 to 150.00	0.50
150.01 to 200.00	0.60

SPECIAL HANDLING FEES

Weight	Fee
Not more than 2 pounds	$0.25
More than 2 pounds but not more than 10 pounds	0.35
More than 10 pounds	0.40

The clerk is preparing the shipping charges for three customers' packages. He has collected data for each package.

Package 1: 20 pounds, parcel post, to zone 4

Package 2: 15 pounds, parcel post, insured for $50.00, to zone 6

Package 3: 4 pounds 3 ounces, special handling, insured for $75.00, to zone 2

a. Organize the data for each of the three packages the clerk must mail.

b. Calculate the total cost of mailing each package.

c. What appears to be the biggest portion of the cost of mailing packages—postage, insurance, or handling fees?

d. The clerk's postage data may be out-of-date. Where might you go to find more current data of this type?

EXERCISE 9: Virginia does the payroll for a small contractor. Each week she collects the data for the hourly employees and calculates their total earnings. Each employee is paid at an hourly rate. Overtime is paid at 1½ times the hourly rate, for all time over 40 hours per week. This week's hourly data are shown below.

Daily hours worked

Name	Mon	Tue	Wed	Thu	Fri
Brooks	8.0	7.5	6.5	9.5	8.5
Clark	7.0	6.0	7.0	7.0	7.0
Holt	8.5	8.0	10.0	9.5	9.0
Nichols	10.0	11.0	9.5	9.5	10.0
Pierce	9.0	9.0	9.0	9.0	8.0
Tyler	7.5	10.5	12.0	8.0	8.0

Virginia also uses a list of the hourly rates for the employees.

Hourly rate

Name	$ per hour
Brooks	$7.80
Clark	8.80
Holt	8.50
Nichols	7.20
Pierce	7.40
Tyler	7.10

a. Collect and organize the data to show the total hours worked by each employee.

b. Interpret the data to find the hours each employee worked at the regular pay rate, and the hours each worked at the overtime pay rate.

c. Use the pay-rate data to determine each employee's pay rate for overtime work.

d. Interpret the pay data and the hours-worked data computed above to calculate the gross pay each worker is due.

EXERCISE 10: A husband and wife are trying to keep the food budget for their family of five under $500 per month. They also want to ensure that everybody has a balanced diet. So they've set up the following guidelines for spending their $500:

Food type	% of total $
Meat	30%
Produce	20%
Dairy products	15%
Breads & pastries	6%
Canned goods	20%
Miscellaneous items	9%

a. Using the data provided above, organize a table and calculate the amount of money the couple can spend each month on each food type.

b. The wife summarizes their actual purchases for last month, as shown below.

Food type	Purchases
Meat	$17, $22, $36, $12, $43
Produce	$10, $18, $5, $9, $21, $19
Dairy products	$18, $22, $19, $20, $17, $12
Breads & pastries	$8, $5, $12, $6, $16, $3, $8
Canned goods	$12, $17, $31, $18, $22, $20
Miscellaneous items	$19, $1, $9, $27, $4

Using the actual purchase data from the wife's records, compute the total purchases for each food type.

c. Interpret the table of actual purchases. Were any items "over budget" during the last month?

EXERCISE 11: A technician is servicing a high-temperature oven for a laboratory. The oven operates around 800°C. The customer wants the technician to recommend the correct type of thermocouple wire to sense the temperature in the oven during certain experiments. The technician checks some catalogs and collects the data as follows.

Thermocouple wire characteristics and prices

Type	Temp range (°C)	Cost per foot
T	0 to 350	$0.50
J	0 to 750	0.55
E	0 to 900	0.67
K	0 to 1250	0.73

a. Interpret the data to determine which type of thermocouple wire will meet the customer's need.

b. For the wires the technician recommends, what would it cost to purchase 125 feet?

c. Use the calculated purchase costs to determine which wire the technician should recommend for minimum cost to the customer.

EXERCISE 12: A shop manager is working on a project to produce a new electronic device that requires some shop work. Part of the planning is to draw up a schedule of time needed for the shop work. The device the manager is designing is made up of parts with which the manager has experience. Her records for the common parts that might be used show the required shop times listed below.

Required shop times for common parts

Part number	Time at lathe	Time at drill press	Time at milling machine	Time at grinding machine
1	14 min 10 sec	4 min 30 sec	17 min 20 sec	8 min 30 sec
2	15 min 20 sec	4 min 40 sec	16 min 40 sec	9 min 15 sec
3	13 min 30 sec	4 min 15 sec	18 min 10 sec	8 min 25 sec
4	14 min 20 sec	4 min 15 sec	16 min 50 sec	7 min 20 sec
5	15 min 15 sec	4 min 50 sec	17 min 25 sec	9 min 30 sec
6	14 min 50 sec	4 min 10 sec	17 min 50 sec	8 min 45 sec
7	15 min 05 sec	4 min 15 sec	17 min 10 sec	8 min 30 sec
8	12 min 50 sec	4 min 25 sec	18 min 35 sec	7 min 45 sec
Totals	112 min 200 sec	32 min 200 sec	136 min 240 sec	64 min 240 sec

The manager is considering several possible methods of construction. Each method consists of a slightly different combination of the common parts. Her arrangements are listed below.

Part combinations being considered

Combination	Parts needed
1	1,3,4
2	1,3,7
3	2,4,8
4	3,7,8

a. Collect and organize the time data for each of the manager's possible combinations.

b. Interpret the data to determine which combination will take the least amount of shop time to construct.

EXERCISE 13: A technician works in an electronics repair shop. On the technician's current work order, a customer reports an unstable performance of the equipment. The technician decides to monitor the voltage output of the 24-volt power supply. The specification manual states the power supply must be stable to 24 volts ±0.25 volt (that is, 23.75 to 24.25 volts). The technician collects data every hour, shown below.

WO#05237
Power supply voltage

	Time	Voltage (V)
(power on)	9:10 A.M.	23.56
	10:00 A.M.	23.80
	11:00 A.M.	23.92
	12:10 P.M.	24.10
	1:10 P.M.	24.12
	2:05 P.M.	24.28

a. The technician already has collected and organized the data. Use the data to determine the average output of the power supply during the test period.

b. Interpret the test data to find the range of the voltage readings during the test period (that is, the highest minus the lowest reading).

c. Should the technician report a problem with the power supply?

d. Plot the technician's data, using time as the bottom axis (9 A.M. to 2 P.M.), and voltage as the side axis (22 V to 26 V). Does there appear to be any trend in the output of the power supply through the day? If so, indicate the trend on the graph. Is there any good reason to plot the data?

EXERCISE 14: An electrician is wiring a new hospital. He keeps a record in a pocket notebook of the supplies he uses each day. His supervisor asks him to summarize his use of supplies for each week. His notebook records are shown below.

Monday

375 ft BX cable, 25 ft of #12 wire, 10 receptacle (Rec.) boxes, 100 ft of #24 wire, 125 ft of BX cable, 20 Rec. boxes

Tuesday

50 ft of #10 wire, 75 ft of BX cable, 175 ft of BX cable, 15 ft of #0 wire, 100 ft of #14 wire

Wednesday

750 ft of BX cable, 12 ft of #0 wire, 65 ft of #12 wire, 80 ft of #10 wire

Thursday

40 ft of #10 wire, 25 Rec. boxes, 30 ft of #12 wire, 18 ft of #10 wire

Friday

45 ft of BX cable, 50 ft of #18 wire

a. Organize the data in a convenient form to determine the totals for each type of material the electrician used this week.

b. Which type of wire or cable does the electrician use the most?

EXERCISE 15: A supervisor oversees the assembling of custom radio kits. The assembly job requires cutting and packaging a number of different wire lengths and quantities. The bill of materials for this kit gives the following information.

Radio kit HX2400
Wire material list

Wire code	Quantity	Length (cm)
1354	17	6.0
1354	6	10.0
2269	10	10.0
3196	1	50.0
6002	6	18.0
8259	25	4.5
9271	14	12.0

The supervisor wishes to investigate the cost of this radio kit. She has a pricing guide that identifies the price per unit length of wire for the different types of wire. With this list she can create a cost sheet for the wire.

Wire pricing chart

Wire code	Length range (cm)	Price/cm
1354	0 – 10	$0.045
1354	> 10	0.025
2269	0 – 5	0.060
2269	> 5	0.040
3196	0 – 10	0.015
3196	11 – 50	0.010
3196	> 50	0.007
6002	0 – 5	0.100
6002	> 5	0.075
8259	any length	0.250
9271	0 – 10	0.030
9271	> 10	0.020

a. Collect the data from the bill of materials and the pricing chart, and organize them in a table. Show, for each wire code needed in the radio kit, the total length needed and price per centimeter.

b. Use these data to determine the total cost of each wire code in the kit, and the total wire cost for the kit.

EXERCISE 16: An auto mechanic has just completed an engine overhaul for a customer. The mechanic's supervisor asks him to determine the cost of the repair job. The mechanic keeps a list of time worked and the parts used. He also has a parts price list. Each is shown below.

<table>
<tr><td colspan="2" align="center">**Parts used**</td><td colspan="2" align="center">**Time spent**</td></tr>
<tr><td>Item</td><td>Quantity</td><td>Day</td><td>Hours</td></tr>
<tr><td>Gasket set</td><td>1</td><td>Monday</td><td>8.0</td></tr>
<tr><td>Ring set</td><td>1</td><td>Tuesday</td><td>7.0</td></tr>
<tr><td>Valves</td><td>8</td><td>Wednesday</td><td>6.5</td></tr>
<tr><td>Wrist pins</td><td>8</td><td>Thursday</td><td>8.5</td></tr>
<tr><td>Valve springs</td><td>16</td><td>Friday</td><td>7.0</td></tr>
<tr><td>Rod bearings</td><td>8</td><td></td><td></td></tr>
<tr><td>Main bearings</td><td>5</td><td></td><td></td></tr>
<tr><td>Valve seals</td><td>16</td><td></td><td></td></tr>
<tr><td>Timing chain</td><td>1</td><td></td><td></td></tr>
</table>

Price list

Item number	Description	Unit price
88465	Valve spring	$ 1.42
75648	Main bearing	2.76
76654	Valve	4.19
66154	Ring set	29.98
55412	Gasket set	42.19
34567	Headlight	8.50
33345	Fuel pump	68.75
25865	Wrist pin	2.11
25432	Rod bearing	1.62
56875	Valve seal	0.32
89565	Muffler	38.50
65485	Timing chain	39.95

a. Organize a table of data showing the parts used, the unit price for each, and the price for the quantity used.

b. If the company charges $20.50 per hour for labor, compute the cost of labor for this job.

c. What is the total cost of this job (parts and labor)?

EXERCISE 17: A technician is analyzing the current drain on an automotive electric system. She has found a chart that shows the current required by various components. The chart is shown below.

Current drain for automotive components

Equipment item	Current required (amps)
1. Turn-signal lights	5
2. Door lights (courtesy/dome)	3
3. Headlights (hi-beam)	14
4. Headlights (lo-beam)	13
5. Electric window (up or down)	5
6. Air conditioner	10
7. Heater, low	8
8. Heater, high	10
9. De-icer	16
10. Power seat	15
11. Radio	1
12. Emergency warning lights	14

The technician wants to check the current required by several combinations of components. Her plan is listed in the following table.

Test plan for current checks

Test no.	Items to turn ON
1	3, 6, 7, 9
2	2, 6, 11,12
3	3, 5, 6, 12
4	4, 7, 10, 11

The technician measures the current drain on the battery for each of the tests and lists the results in the table shown below.

Test data for current checks

Test no.	Measured current
1	46 amps
2	32 amps
3	44 amps
4	39 amps

a. Collect the current data for each test and organize them in a table.

b. Interpret the technician's test data to determine which (if any) of the tests resulted in <u>more than one amp</u> over the specified current drain.

EXERCISE 18: An upholstery shop charges $300 per sofa and $160 per chair for labor to reupholster furniture. For the upholstery material, the shop charges "by the yard." A customer has asked for an estimated cost to reupholster furniture from a college dormitory. The shop manager inspects the furniture and finds there are 14 sofas and 6 chairs, as follows.

Sofas	Chairs
2: item 5	1: item 33
1: item 8	1: item 45
6: item 10	1: item 54
5: item 2	3: item 57

The manager uses a pictorial chart to guide her in determining the amount of upholstery material needed, as shown below.

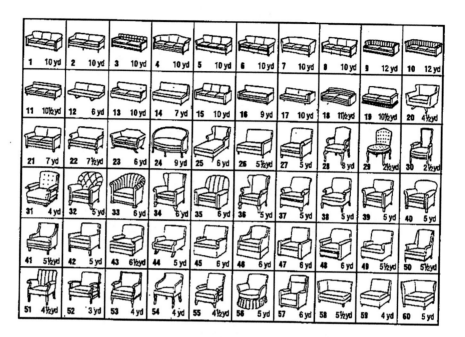

a. Determine how much upholstery material the shop will use to cover the sofas and the chairs.

b. Determine the labor charges needed to fill this customer's order.

c. The upholstery material selected by the customer costs $35 per yard. Determine the material cost to fill this customer's order.

d. What is the total cost estimate for the customer: materials and labor?

EXERCISE 19: An estimator's helper for a plumbing contractor is preparing estimates for a job. The blueprint calls for the installation of several different pumps. The estimator lists the number required and pump descriptions, as shown below.

2 each: 3000 gallons per minute, 10-inch suction, 150 horsepower

1 each: 500 gallons per minute, 3-inch suction, 25 horsepower

3 each: 1200 gallons per minute, 6-inch suction, 60 horsepower

1 each: 6000 gallons per minute, 14-inch suction, 300 horsepower

The estimator has an hourly estimation chart for installation of pumps and motors, as shown below. The chart lists labor hours required to install each pump, and also how many labor hours are needed to perform the necessary electrical work.

Installation of pumps and motors
Net labor hours per unit

Gallons Per Minute	Head Feet	Suction Inches	Discharge Inches	Motor Horsepower	Approx. Weight Pounds	PERSONHOURS	
						Pump	Electrical
5	200	1	1	1	127	5.6	4.0
30	50	1	1	1	125	5.6	4.0
50	600	1	1	1½	169	5.8	5.0
100	125	2½	2	7½	800	13.7	8.0
200	80	2½	2	7½	840	13.8	8.0
200	150	2½	2	15	1050	16.9	11.3
300	130	2½	2	20	1140	17.6	12.8
500	150	3	2½	25	1485	20.2	14.6
700	150	4	3	40	1760	23.9	23.8
900	150	5	4	50	1805	24.6	24.5
1200	150	6	5	60	2695	28.1	25.2
1350	120	6	5	60	1595	20.7	25.2
2000	150	10	8	100	3100	30.6	44.2
3000	150	10	8	150	4870	37.2	50.7
4000	70	10	8	100	2900	30.0	44.2
5000	180	14	12	300	6460	38.4	52.0
6000	160	14	12	300	6460	38.4	52.0
8000	180	16	14	450	12600	60.3	99.0
10000	200	18	16	600	18000	62.4	118.8
	2000			1000	25000	208.0	156.0

a. Collect the data for quantities and descriptions of the required pumps. Organize the data into convenient tabular form.

b. Compute the total labor hours required to install and wire each pump (that is, pump and electrical). Add this to your table of data.

c. How many total labor hours will be required to install all the pumps and motors for this job?

d. If the deadline for having the electrical work finished is three weeks away, how many electricians are needed to finish the job on time? (Assume each will work 40 hours per week.)

EXERCISE 20: A contractor is replacing beveled siding on an old house. The customer wants 8" beveled siding, with 6½" per board exposed to weather. The contractor refers to the carpenter's table shown below to determine how much siding should be allowed for lap and waste when ordering the siding. He knows the house walls are 12' high all around. The floor plan for the outer house walls is shown below.

Table of lap and waste allowances—beveled siding

Width	Exposure to weather	Add for lap and waste
12"	10½"	15%
12"	10"	20%
10"	8½"	18%
10"	8"	24%
8"	6½"	23%
8"	6"	30%
6"	5"	25%
6"	4¾"	32%
6"	4½"	38%
4"	2¾"	51%
4"	2½"	65%

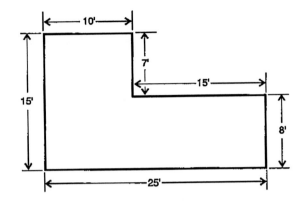

a. Collect and organize the data needed to solve the contractor's problem.

b. Calculate the total area (height times the width) of the outside house walls.

c. Calculate the amount of square footage to allow for lap and waste (percentage times the total area for the proper size siding).

d. How many square feet of beveled siding should the contractor order?

Glossary

Ampere   A name for the unit of current that flows in an electrical circuit. Electrical current is measured with an instrument known as an ammeter.

Approximate value   A value that is nearly correct or true. For example, a person who gives the temperature as 90°F, when it is actually 92.7°F, is giving an approximate value for the temperature.

Approximation   The process of approaching, or coming near to, a true or exact value, answer, quantity, and so on. For example, the approximation to the true width of a human hair becomes better and better as a more accurate instrument—such as a micrometer—is used to make the measurement.

Area   A measure of the amount of surface. The area of a flat rectangular surface can be calculated by multiplying the length of the surface by its width. For example, if a book cover is 10 inches long and 7 inches wide, its area is 10 inches times 7 inches, or 70 **square inches.**

Axis   A reference line used in making graphs. Generally, one of the axes is a horizontal line—sometimes called the *x*-axis—and the other is a vertical line—sometimes called the *y*-axis. The horizontal and vertical axes are perpendicular to one another. They start at a common point, usually the lower left corner of the graph. The common point is referred to as the origin of the graph.

Bar graph   A type of graph that uses side-by-side horizontal bars or vertical bars of different lengths to compare different items of information.

Calculator memory   A way to store a number in the calculator. A number shown in the display window can be stored in the calculator memory by pressing a key designated by such symbols as M_{in}, $x{\rightarrow}M$, **M+**, or **M→**. The number stored (placed in memory) can be retrieved—or "recalled"—for later use. This is done by pressing a key usually designated **RM,** for Recall Memory. The number in memory can be removed—or cleared—by using the **CM** key, by turning the calculator off, or, if that fails, by entering "0" in the memory.

Caliper   A tool used for precision length measurements. It has a fixed jaw, a sliding jaw, and a calibrated scale.

Celsius   The scale of temperature measurement used in the metric system. On a Celsius scale—formerly known as the Centigrade scale—water freezes at 0° and boils at 100°. The Celsius scale is related to the Fahrenheit scale of temperature measurement by the formula

$$°C = ⅝ (°F - 32)$$

Centi–   A prefix indicating "a hundredth part." For example, a <u>centi</u>meter is one hundredth of a meter (0.01 m).

Circle graph   A type of graph that is circular in shape. The circle graph compares different information by assigning "pie sections" of different sizes to the various categories of information.

**Clear
(a calculator
operation)**   Remove the number and/or operation from a calculator display, storage area, or both. This is done with the "C" button on the calculator or, on some calculators, with the on/off button.

Collect   Obtain and gather data to be used in solving a problem.

**Computational
solution**   Using arithmetic operations and numbers to get an answer to a problem.

Data   Factual information collected to solve a problem.

**Decimal
fraction**   A proper or improper fraction written in a form that includes a decimal point and numbers to the right and (sometimes) left of the decimal point. For example, the proper fraction ⅜ is equal to 0.375 when written as a decimal fraction. The improper fraction 1⁰⁄₈ is equal to 1.25.

**Decimal
number**   A number written in a form that involves a decimal point and digits to the right and left of the decimal point. For example, the numbers 1.25, 0.375, and 197.2 all are written as decimals.

Denominator   The number below (or to the right of) the fraction line for any proper or improper fraction. For example, the number "8" is the denominator for the fractions ⅜ and 1⁰⁄₈.

Digit   Any of the ten numerals 0, 1, 2, 3, 4, 5, 6, 7, 8, and 9. In our number system, all numbers, whether decimals, fractions, or whole numbers are written using these ten digits.

Display window	The flat area of the calculator that visually displays the numbers keyed into the calculator and the answers or results of mathematics operations generated by the calculator.
Equivalent	"Equal to" but not necessarily "identical to." For example, the fraction ¼ is equivalent to the decimal fraction 0.25, and each is equivalent to 25 percent.
Estimate	(Verb) To calculate an approximate answer. To estimate the answer, the numbers are rounded to make the calculations easier. By comparing an estimated answer with the answer from your calculator, you can check the answer shown on your calculator. For example, 2.1×4.9 is about $2 \times 5 = 10$. Compare 10 (estimated answer) to 10.29 (calculator answer). They are close, so you can be reasonably confident of the calculated answer. However, if your calculator gives you an answer of 102.9, you can be sure you need to do the calculation again.
	(Noun) The approximate value or answer given in place of the true or exact value.
Estimated answer	An approximate answer based on experience, an intelligent guess, or a rounding of numbers at each step in the actual calculations.
Exact value (true value)	That one value the approximate answer approaches, as the approximation or measurement technique gets better and better. For example, when dealing with a measurement of size, weight, or temperature, a measuring instrument provides only an approximate value at best, even though a true (exact) value may exist. In other instances, involving numerical operations, the exact answer exists and is readily found. For example, the operation $15 \div 2$ has the exact answer of 7.5. For the purposes of this series, an estimate or approximate answer is always compared to the exact (or true) value to determine how "good" the estimate or approximate answer is.

Extrapolate   To extend a graph to find values beyond the known range. For example, in a graph of Celsius and Fahrenheit temperatures, the boiling point of water (100°C, 212°F) and the freezing point of water (0°C, 32°F) can be graphed. A straight line can be drawn between these points. Then the desired Celsius temperature can be extrapolated by extending the line and reading the value that is equal to 300°F.

Factor   A number that can be evenly divided into another number. For example, 3 is a factor of 9.

Fahrenheit   The scale of temperature measurement used in the English system. On a Fahrenheit scale, water freezes at 32° and boils at 212°. The Fahrenheit scale is related to the Celsius scale of temperature measurement by the formula

$$°F = \frac{9}{5} °C + 32$$

Fraction   A number such as ⅓, ⅗, or ²⁰⁄₉ written with one whole number over another. The number on the top is called the numerator. The number on the bottom is called the denominator. The line that separates the two numbers is called the fraction line. The fraction line indicates a division operation.

Gram   The basic unit of mass ("weight") in the metric system of measurement, equal to about ¹⁄₂₈ of an ounce. (It is the mass of one milliliter of distilled water at 4°C.)

Graph   A diagram that pictures data or information in a way that makes it easier to understand. You use graphs to show the largest or smallest values of data, trends, and patterns. Common graphs are bar graphs, circle graphs, and line graphs.

Graphical solution   Use of graphs, drawings, or diagrams to find an answer to a problem.

Graph units   The particular values assigned to represent the information displayed on a graph. For example, the graph units for time labeled along a horizontal axis may be chosen as seconds, hours, days, months, or years, depending on the length of time to be represented. Similarly, if cost is labeled along a vertical axis, the graph units may be chosen as cents, dollars, thousands of dollars, millions of dollars, and so on, depending on the range of cost to be shown.

Grid lines   The horizontal and vertical lines drawn parallel to the horizontal and vertical axes of a graph. Taken together these intersecting lines form a grid. Each horizontal line represents a specific value of the information labeled along the vertical axis. Each vertical line represents a specific value of the information labeled along the horizontal axis.

Horizontal   A direction parallel to the horizon or level with the ground. On a graph drawn on paper, it refers to an axis or grid line that is drawn from left to right, parallel to the bottom of the page.

Improper fraction   Any fraction, such as $\frac{9}{8}$, $\frac{5}{3}$, or $\frac{10}{10}$, whose value is equal to or larger than one. The numerator of an improper fraction is always equal to or larger than the denominator.

Input ("key in")   The operation of pressing keys on the calculator keyboard to enter numbers or instructions.

Interpolate   To estimate a value from a graph or table that is between known or labeled values. For example, on the number line below, the point is halfway between 10 and 20, so the value of 15 is estimated. This process is called "interpolation."

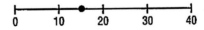

Interpret   Explain or arrive at a conclusion based on a study of data.

Keyboard   That part of the calculator made up of keys for numbers, operations, and instructions.

Kilo–   A prefix indicating "a thousand." For example, a <u>kilo</u>gram is 1000 grams, and a <u>kilo</u>watt is 1000 watts.

Line graph	A series of points, plotted between the horizontal and vertical axes of a graph, that form a line when connected to one another. Each point on the line represents a specific value of the quantities labeled along the horizontal and vertical axes of the graph.
List	A way you can use to organize data. A list is similar to a table, except that you consider only one characteristic. Thus, you usually display the data in a single column.
Liter	The basic unit of volume in the metric system of measurement, equal to 1.0567 liquid quarts. (It is officially defined as the volume of 1 kilogram of distilled water at 4°C.)
Mathematics operations	The arithmetic processes of adding, subtracting, multiplying, and dividing.
Meter	The basic unit of length in the metric system of measurement, equal to 39.37 inches. (It is officially defined on the basis of the wavelength of krypton light.)
Milli–	A prefix indicating "a thousandth part." For example, a <u>milli</u>meter is one thousandth of a meter (0.001 m) and a <u>milli</u>liter is one thousandth of a liter (0.001 L).
Mixed number	A combination of a whole number and a fraction. For example, $9\frac{7}{16}$ is a mixed number made up of the whole number 9 and the fraction $\frac{7}{16}$.
Negative number	A number less than zero. Negative numbers are distinguished from positive numbers by the symbol (–). Thus –3 means three less than zero, while +3 means three more than zero. With a calculator, a positive number shown in the display window (such as +5) can be changed to a negative number (–5) by pressing the key labeled (+/–).
Numerator	The number above (or to the left of) the fraction line for any proper or improper fraction. For example, the number 3 is the numerator for the fractions $\frac{3}{10}$ and $\frac{3}{2}$.

Opposite operations	A mathematics operation that **cancels** the effect of another operation. For example, **subtracting** 7 from a number is canceled by the opposite operation of **adding** 7. That is, $19 - 7 + 7 = 19$. Hence, addition and subtraction are opposite operations. Similarly, multiplication and division are opposite operations.
Organize	Arrange data in an orderly fashion so that they will be easier for you to interpret.
Origin	A unique point on a graph determined by the intersection of the horizontal and vertical axes of the graph. Numbers labeled along the horizontal and vertical axes of the graph generally have their lowest values at the origin. In some cases, the numbers labeled along the two axes begin with zero values at the origin. In that case, the origin is also referred to as the "zero point."
Parentheses (referring to calculators)	Parentheses on the calculator are used to group numbers and operations so that the numbers and operations are carried out in a specified order.
Percent	Parts per hundred. One percent of something means the same as one hundredth of something. The word "percent" often is represented by the symbol %. Thus, 25 percent and 25% mean the same thing—twenty-five hundredths of something.
Perimeter	Distance around an object.
Plan for solution	A method or scheme of working out the solution to a problem.
Problem	Any situation that presents a question requiring a solution.
Problem-solving method	A method that usually involves four **main** steps: 1. Understand the problem. 2. Develop a plan. 3. Carry out the plan. 4. Check the results.
Proper fraction	Any fraction, such as ⅜, ⅕, or ⅚, whose value is less than one. The numerator of a proper fraction is always less than the denominator.

Reasonable answer
An answer, obtained as a result of a calculation, that makes sense in the context of the problem. A calculated answer is said to be "reasonable" when it agrees more or less closely with an answer to the problem obtained by an estimate or approximate calculation. For example, if the answer to the calculation of the area of a triangle came out to be 115.27 square inches, and a correct estimate for the same calculation gave 110 square inches, you would conclude that the answer of 115.27 square inches is a "reasonable" answer. If, however, the calculated answer came out to be 1152.7 square inches—and the correct estimate gave 110 square inches—you would conclude that 1152.7 square inches is not a "reasonable answer." You would then recheck your calculation to find where an error had been made.

Recall memory
Retrieve a number stored in the calculator memory, usually by pressing a calculator key designated **RM**. When **RM** is pressed, the number stored in calculator memory is shown in the display window and can be used in calculations.

Reduced fraction
A fraction in its basic or simplest form, whose numerator and denominator contain no common factors other than 1. For example, the fraction $15/20$ is not a reduced fraction because both the numerator "15" and the denominator "20" contain the common factor 5. The fraction $15/20$ can be "reduced" by dividing both the numerator and denominator by 5, as follows:

$$\frac{15}{20} = \frac{15 \div 5}{20 \div 5} = \frac{3}{4}$$

The fraction $3/4$ now has no common factors in the numerator "3" and the denominator "4" other than 1. The fraction $3/4$ is therefore a reduced fraction, in its simplest form.

Resistance
A term used to indicate the opposition to current flow in electrical circuits. The higher the resistance of a circuit element, the more voltage is needed to produce a given value of current.

Rounding Expressing to a round number. A number is rounded by following certain rules.

a. Identify the position of the last digit to be saved.

b. The digit to be saved is increased by 1 if the digit to the right is 5 or greater.

c. The digit to be saved remains unchanged if the digit to the right is 4 or less.

d. All digits to the right of the decimal point that are to be rounded are dropped. All digits to the left of the decimal point that are to be rounded are replaced with 0s to keep the decimal point in the proper place. For example, 17.324, rounded to the nearest tenth, is 17.3. The digits 2 and 4 are dropped. Similarly, 186,872, rounded to the nearest thousand, is 187,000. The digits 8, 7, and 2 are replaced by zeros.

Sample A small amount of data that you collect from a large amount of available information. Generally you hope that this sample of data will provide a good indication of what larger amounts of data will predict.

Solution The answer to the question presented by a problem.

Source In this book, a person, book, document, situation, and so on that can provide facts to help you solve a problem.

Table An organized array of information—usually numbers—arranged in appropriately labeled rows and columns.

Tally A way you can organize data that is useful when counting is involved. Tallying often is done with "tic" marks, in groups of five.

Trend A basis for interpreting a change in data, normally used with graphs. An observation is made about the values of the data that have similar behavior, such as values that are continually increasing or decreasing. For example, consider a graph that shows the cost of living for the past 24 months. It indicates the cost of living has increased steadily each month. This steady increase is seen as a trend that may continue unless other economic factors come into play.

Unending repeating decimal	A fraction, such as ⅓ and ⅔, that results in unending, repeating numbers when changed to a decimal fraction. For example, ⅓ becomes 0.33333333... with no end to the string of threes. That's because 3 does not divide evenly into 1. Likewise, the fraction ⅔ becomes 0.66666666..., another string, this one of unending sixes.
Unit conversion ratio	A fraction, or ratio, that equals **one,** having a quantity with a certain unit of measure in the numerator, and a quantity with a different unit of measure in the denominator. This ratio is used to convert between units. For example, a unit ratio for converting inches to centimeters is

$$\frac{1 \text{ inch}}{2.54 \text{ centimeters}} \text{ or } \frac{0.3937 \text{ inch}}{1 \text{ centimeter}}$$

Units place (ones place)	The first place to the left of the decimal point. For example, the decimal number 84.7 has the digit 8 written in the "tens" place, the digit 4 written in the "ones" place, and the digit 7 written in the "tenths" place.
Vernier	A short scale that slides along a longer scale. It permits a more accurate reading of fractional parts of divisions on the longer scale.
Vertical	A direction perpendicular to the horizon or perpendicular to the level ground. On a graph drawn on paper, it refers to an axis or grid line that is drawn from top to bottom, parallel to a side of the page.
Volt	A name for the unit of voltage in electrical circuits. Electrical voltage is measured with an instrument known as a voltmeter.
Volume	A measure of the amount of space enclosed in a container. For example, the total space inside a box is equal to the volume of the box. The space inside a ball is equal to the volume of the ball. Volume is measured in units such as cubic centimeters, cubic inches, or cubic feet. The volume of a box can be calculated by multiplying the length of the box by its height and this result by its width. For example, if a box is 11 inches long, 12 inches high, and 10 inches wide, its volume is 11 inches times 12 inches times 10 inches, or 1320 cubic inches.

Whole numbers Any one of the "counting" numbers, such as 0, 1, 2, 3, 4, 5, 6, 7, 8, 9, 10, 11, 12... and so on. A whole number has no fractional part and no digits to the right of the decimal point. Thus, the numbers ½, 10.2, and 2⅕ are **not** whole numbers.

Window The clear, screen-like region on the face of the calculator where numbers are displayed.

Zero point The origin or point on a graph where the horizontal and vertical axes intersect. The origin is referred to as the zero point when the numbers labeled along the horizontal and vertical axes begin with zero values at this point. The zero point is located generally at the lower left corner of the graph.

Appendix A

Student Reference Materials

The following are resources you will find useful in completing the laboratory and student activities.

TABLES OF CONVERSION FACTORS

To convert from meters to inches, for example, find the row labeled 1 "meter" and the column labeled "in."
The conversion factor is 39.37. Thus, 1 meter = 39.37 in.

LENGTH

	cm	m	km	in.	ft	yd	mi
1 centimeter	1	0.01	10^{-5}	0.3937	3.281×10^{-2}	1.094×10^{-2}	6.214×10^{-6}
1 meter	100	1	10^{-3}	39.37	3.281	1.094	6.214×10^{-4}
1 kilometer	10^5	1000	1	3.937×10^4	3281	1094	0.6214
1 inch	2.54	0.0254	2.54×10^{-5}	1	0.0833	0.0278	1.578×10^{-5}
1 foot	30.48	0.3048	3.048×10^{-4}	12	1	0.3333	1.894×10^{-4}
1 yard	91.44	0.9144	9.144×10^{-4}	36	3	1	5.682×10^{-4}
1 mile	1.6093×10^5	1609.3	1.6093	6.336×10^4	5280	1760	1

AREA

	cm^2	m^2	in^2	ft^2	acre	mi^2	ha
1 square centimeter	1	10^{-4}	0.1550	1.076×10^{-3}	2.471×10^{-8}	3.861×10^{-11}	10^{-8}
1 square meter	10^4	1	1550	10.76	2.471×10^{-4}	3.861×10^{-7}	10^{-4}
1 square inch	6.452	6.452×10^{-4}	1	6.944×10^{-3}	1.594×10^{-7}	2.491×10^{-10}	6.452×10^{-8}
1 square foot	929.0	0.09290	144	1	2.296×10^{-5}	3.587×10^{-8}	9.29×10^{-6}
1 acre	4.047×10^7	4047	6.273×10^6	43,560	1	1.563×10^{-3}	0.4047
1 square mile	2.590×10^{10}	2.590×10^6	4.007×10^9	2.788×10^7	640	1	259
1 hectare	10^8	10^4	1.55×10^7	1.076×10^5	2.471	3.861×10^{-3}	1

NOTE: The number 3.281×10^{-2} is equivalent to 0.03281, and the number 3.937×10^4 is equivalent to 39,370. If you have difficulty understanding this, please consult your teacher.

VOLUME (CAPACITY)

	cm^3	m^3	in^3	ft^3	L	oz	gal
1 cubic centimeter	1	10^{-6}	0.06102	3.531×10^{-5}	1.000×10^{-3}	0.03381	2.642×10^{-4}
1 cubic meter	10^6	1	6.102×10^4	35.31	1000.	3.381×10^4	264.2
1 cubic inch	16.39	1.639×10^{-5}	1	5.787×10^{-4}	0.01639	0.5541	4.329×10^{-3}
1 cubic foot	2.832×10^4	0.02832	1728	1	28.32	957.5	7.480
1 liter	1000.	1.000×10^{-3}	61.03	0.03532	1	33.81	0.2642
1 ounce	29.57	2.957×10^{-5}	1.805	1.044×10^{-3}	0.02957	1	7.813×10^{-3}
1 gallon	3785	3.785×10^{-3}	231	0.1337	3.785	128	1

1 gallon = 4 quarts (qt) = 8 pints (pt) = 16 cups (c)
1 cup (c) = 8 ounces (oz) = 16 tablespoons (tbsp) = 48 teaspoons

MASS / WEIGHT

	g	kg	oz	lb	ton (short)	ton (metric)
1 gram	1	10^{-3}	0.03527	2.205×10^{-3}	1.102×10^{-6}	10^{-6}
1 kilogram	10^3	1	35.27	2.205	1.102×10^{-3}	10^{-3}
1 ounce	28.35	0.02835	1	0.0625	3.125×10^{-5}	2.835×10^{-5}
1 pound	453.6	0.4536	16	1	0.0005	4.536×10^{-4}
1 ton (short)	9.072×10^5	907.2	3.2×10^4	2000	1	0.9072
1 ton (metric)	10^6	10^3	3.527×10^4	2.205×10^3	1.102	1

NOTE: The number 3.281×10^{-2} is equivalent to 0.03281, and the number 3.937×10^4 is equivalent to 39,370. If you have difficulty understanding this, please consult your teacher.

ANGLE

	'	°	rad	rev
1 minute	1	0.01667	2.909×10^{-4}	4.630×10^{-5}
1 degree	60	1	0.01745	2.778×10^{-3}
1 radian	3438	57.30	1	0.1592
1 revolution	2.16×10^4	360	6.283	1

TIME

	s	min	hr	d*	y*
1 second	1	0.01667	2.788×10^{-4}	1.157×10^{-5}	3.169×10^{-8}
1 minute	60	1	0.01667	6.944×10^{-4}	1.901×10^{-6}
1 hour	3600	60	1	0.04167	1.141×10^{-4}
1 day*	8.640×10^4	1440	24	1	2.738×10^{-3}
1 year*	3.156×10^7	5.259×10^5	8766	365.3	1

*sidereal

NOTE: The number 3.281×10^{-2} is equivalent to 0.03281, and the number 3.937×10^4 is equivalent to 39,370. If you have difficulty understanding this, please consult your teacher.

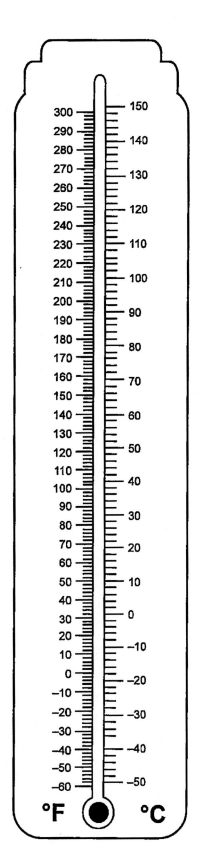

Dual-scale Thermometer

(This page is intentionally blank.)

Appendix B

How to Use the Accu-Line™ Drawing Aid

The Accu-Line™ is a drawing aid. It is useful in making sketches with perpendicular and parallel lines and drawing angles with a specified measure.

The Accu-Line™ guides a ballpoint pen or a mechanical pencil in narrow grooves along straight lines. With the Accu-Line™, you can draw parallel lines as close as 0.5 mm.

To draw a vertical line, place the point of the pen or pencil at the starting point for the line. Tilt the top of the pen or pencil toward the bottom of the pad and pull the pencil in the direction you are drawing, pressing on the paper with a normal writing pressure. See illustration **A** below.

To draw a horizontal line, place the point of the pen or pencil at the starting point for the line. Tilt the top of the pen or pencil to the right if you are right handed and to the left if you are left handed. **Pull** the pen or pencil in the direction you are drawing, pressing on the paper with a normal writing pressure. See illustration **B** below.

Always tilt the pen or pencil in the direction you are drawing. Always pull the pen or pencil in the direction you are drawing. Never push the pen or pencil.

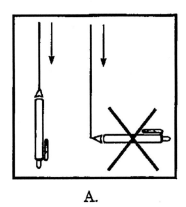

A.

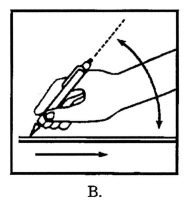

B.

Practice using the Accu-Line™ by sketching the floor plan of your home. Do not worry about the scale. You only need to show the layout of the rooms.

The Accu-Line™ is also useful for drawing angles. A protractor is printed on the Accu-Line™. To draw angles, you must remove the paper you are drawing on from the pad. First, align the left edge of the paper with the vertical scale on the left side of the Accu-Line™. See illustration **C.** Draw a vertical reference line near this reference edge of the paper. Next, without moving the paper, draw a horizontal line on the paper. This line will be one of the sides of the angle you want to draw. Now, rotate the paper and align the reference edge of the paper on the specified angle measure of the protractor (for example, on the 30° mark for a 30° angle). See illustration **D**. Hold the paper firmly in position and draw a vertical line on the paper that crosses the horizontal line. The angle between the vertical line just drawn and the horizontal line is the desired angle.

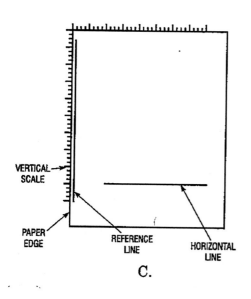

C.

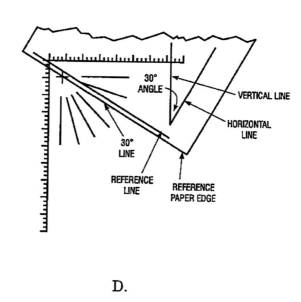

D.

Practice drawing the following angles with the Accu-Line™:

     30°angle.

     45° angle.

     75°angle.

Practice using the Accu-Line™ to draw lines and angles of any shape.

(This page is intentionally blank.)